GENETIC DISORDERS

Peter D Turnpenny

with Dorothy Marsh and Sarah Lucas

BAAF
ADOPTION
& FOSTERING

Published by
British Association for Adoption & Fostering
(BAAF)
Saffron House
6–10 Kirby Street
London EC1N 8TS
www.baaf.org.uk

Charity registration 275689 (England and Wales)
and SC039337 (Scotland)

Section I © Peter D Turnpenny, 2014; Section II © Individual
authors, 2014

British Library Cataloguing in Publication Data
A catalogue record for this book is available from the British Library

ISBN 978 1 910039 05 2

Project management by Jo Francis, Publications Department, BAAF
Designed and typeset by Fravashi Aga
Printed in Great Britain by the Lavenham Press
Trade distribution by Turnaround Publisher Services, Unit 3,
Olympia Trading Estate, Coburg Road, London N22 6TZ

BAAF is the leading UK-wide membership organisation for all those
concerned with adoption, fostering and child care issues.

Contents

Acknowledgements

I am grateful to all those patients and families, especially those where adoption and fostering have featured significantly, from whom I have learned so much.

Note about the authors

Dr Peter Turnpenny is Consultant Clinical Geneticist at the Royal Devon & Exeter Hospital, and Honorary Associate Professor at the University of Exeter Medical School. After a ten-year career in paediatrics, including seven years working in the Middle East, he retrained in Clinical Genetics in Aberdeen and moved to his current position in September 1993. In 1995, he wrote and edited the BAAF book, *Secrets in the Genes: Adoption, inheritance and genetic disease*. He has research or special interests in abnormal spine development, foetal anticonvulsant syndromes, and hypermobility. In 2003, he became the lead author for the established textbook, *Emery's Elements of Medical Genetics*, and the 13th edition (2007) won the BMA Student Textbook Award for 2008. From 2011–13, Dr Turnpenny was President of the Clinical Genetics Society.

Dorothy Marsh

I am a forty-something working mum who spends her life feeling guilty for both being at work and being at home. My free time (ha!) is spent cooking, vegetable gardening, making chutney and finding new excuses not to tidy up. I used to be thinner and drink less, now I pretend to stick to four units a week and steal my daughter's snacks on an all-too-regular basis. I am a passionate, card-carrying adopter and I have never been more tired or happier.

Sarah Lucas

Sarah Lucas lives in central England with her husband Ted and two of their six children. Together with their three home-grown sons, they have cared for over forty children as foster carers, and have three adopted daughters.

The series editor

The editor of this series, **Hedi Argent**, is an established author/editor for BAAF. Her books cover a wide range of family placement topics; she has written several guides and a story book for young children.

Looking behind the label...

Jack has mild learning difficulties and displays some characteristics of ADHD and it is uncertain whether this will increase...

Beth and Mary both have a diagnosis of global developmental delay...

Abigail's birth mother has a history of substance abuse. There is no clear evidence that Abigail was prenatally exposed to drugs but her new family will have to accept some kind of developmental uncertainty...

Jade has some literacy and numeracy difficulties, but has made some improvement with the support of a learning mentor...

Prospective adopters and carers are often faced with the prospect of having to decide whether they can care for a child with a health need or condition they know little about and have no direct experience of. No easy task...

Will Jack's learning difficulties become more severe?
Will Beth and Mary be able to catch up?
When will it be clear whether or not Abigail has been affected by parental substance misuse?
And will Jade need a learning mentor throughout her school life?

It can be difficult to know where to turn for reliable information. What lies behind the diagnoses and "labels" that many looked after children bring with them? And what will it be like to live with them? How will they benefit from family life?

Parenting Matters is a unique series, "inspired" by the terms used – and the need to "decode them" – in profiles of children needing new permanent families. Each title provides expert knowledge about a particular condition, coupled with facts, figures and guidance presented in a straightforward and accessible style. Each book also describes what it is like to parent an affected child, with adopters and foster carers "telling it like it is", sharing their parenting experiences, and offering useful advice. This combination of expert information and first-hand experiences will help readers to gain understanding, and to make informed decisions.

Titles in the series will deal with a wide range of health conditions and steer readers to where they can find more information. They will offer a sound introduction to the topic under consideration and offer a glimpse of what it would be like to live with a "labelled" child. Most importantly, this series will look behind the label and give families the confidence to look more closely at a child whom they otherwise might have passed by.

Keep up with new titles as they are published by signing up to our newsletter on www.baaf.org.uk/bookshop.

Shaila Shah

Titles in this series include:

- *Parenting a Child with Attention Deficit Hyperactivity Disorder*

- *Parenting a Child with Dyslexia*

- *Parenting a Child with Mental Health Issues*

- *Parenting a Child Affected by Parental Substance Misuse*

- *Parenting a Child with Emotional and Behavioural Difficulties*

- *Parenting a Child with Autism Spectrum Disorder*

- *Parenting a Child with Developmental Delay*

Introduction

This book is concerned with genetic disorders, the problems of being "at risk" of genetic disorders, and the effects on children, particularly adopted and looked after children.

The first half of the book looks at the effect of genetics on human health, and explains how genetic disorders may pass through families. It goes on to look at what parents can do when a child, or a child's birth parents, have, or may have, a genetic disease, and explores the issues regarding genetic testing of adopted children.

In the second half of the book, Dorothy Marsh and Sarah Lucas describe their experiences of parenting children with genetic disorders and how this has affected day-to-day family life.

UNDERSTANDING GENETIC DISORDERS

PETER D TURNPENNY

CHAPTER I

Genetics in human health and disease

Stories and discoveries relating to human genetics and genetic disease now feature in our newspapers on virtually a daily basis. Often, this relates to the latest breakthrough in some aspect of reproductive technology such as in-vitro fertilisation (IVF) or a new application of stem cell therapy. However, even as I write this, there is breaking news from a research group that has found a genetic basis for differences in the time taken for individuals to recover from jetlag after a long flight to a distant time zone. A generation ago this was not something that many medical scientists, let alone members of the general public, would have predicted to be strongly embedded in one's genetic code. Indeed, only 25 years ago geneticists who wanted to study the cause of breast cancer which was clearly clustering in families, often occurring at an alarmingly young age, had great difficulty securing research grants because the prevailing wisdom at the time (so recently!) was that breast cancer was not hereditary. Today the general public is well aware that a proportion of breast cancer may run strongly through a family and that genetic testing may be possible to determine whether one might be at high risk. Indeed, a family history of breast cancer is far and away the single most common reason for seeking information and advice from clinical genetic services, amounting to about 40 per cent of all referrals in some centres.

What is meant by "genetic" and other terms?

There are different understandings about the family implications of genetic disease and the terminology needs a little clarification. It may be thought that to describe a medical problem as "genetic" immediately implies a significant risk to other biological family members. But this is only a limited definition of "genetic" because many medical problems with a genetic basis do not necessarily confer a significant "hereditary" risk to the next child, and so the concepts of a "genetic" condition and a "hereditary" condition need to be clarified.

All "hereditary" conditions, essentially, have a genetic basis, but many "genetic" conditions occur as "one-off" events.

A term that is often a source of confusion is "congenital". People may say that a medical problem is "congenital" when they mean "hereditary" or perhaps "genetic". But the term "congenital" simply means that a child is born with a condition that is evident at birth and, while it will include many conditions that have a genetic basis, some of which have hereditary implications, many congenital problems are not apparently genetic at all. For instance, congenital hypothyroidism, for which babies are screened at birth and treatment is started if the diagnosis is confirmed, is very seldom a genetic or hereditary problem. In many cases, the thyroid gland has simply failed to develop and this is due to a disruptive failure during development, i.e. an accident of development that not pre-programmed in the child's genetic make-up.

The pace of new discoveries in human genetics is very swift and is having a huge impact on our understanding of medical conditions and disease, and how these may, or may not, be transmitted through a family. Many advances are being made in our understanding of the genetic causes of intellectual disability, behavioural problems and mental illness, besides the more traditional medical conditions known to have a genetic basis; over the next few years, a great deal more will be learned. We are also moving towards the era of personalised medicine whereby drug treatment for many conditions, for example, certain types of cancer, will be tailored to the patient's genetic make-up, in the knowledge that the standard therapy may not be beneficial or, even worse, cause dangerous side-effects. All this is beginning to affect how we view ourselves and our health, and as the cost of new technologies and genetic testing comes down, so it will become more affordable and accessible. In the future, we may all carry a copy of our complete genetic code, which could be used for screening for disease and susceptibilities, and scrutinised and interrogated whenever necessary.

One of the things we have learned in recent years, since the genome (an organism's hereditary information, encoded in DNA) was fully sequenced, is just how variable is the structure and assembly of DNA between one individual and the next. This variation has been very successfully exploited in DNA fingerprinting to determine paternity, for example, and in forensic science to assist the process of criminal conviction, or eliminate possible suspects. These analyses are generally based on DNA variations that probably bear no great influence over health or disease. Increasingly, though, we are uncovering variations in our DNA (often referred to as "copy number variants" or

CNVs) and rearrangements or imbalances that are significant, particularly in relation to neurodevelopmental disorders and behavioural problems – exactly the sort of issues about which there is heightened concern in adoption. However, many of these variants can only meaningfully be interpreted in the light of investigating the parents and sometimes members of the wider birth family, which may be highly problematic or impossible in adoption scenarios. In the "genetics revolution" that is unfolding, therefore, adopted people may be relatively disadvantaged in terms of interpreting what medical secrets their genome will yield, although they would not be alone because there are obviously other situations where the birth parents and/or other relatives are simply not available.

But there is another use to which analysis of the whole genome might be put in the future. As more and more people take an active interest in their origins and the lives and identities of their ancestors, shown through the rise in popularity of genealogy programmes in the media, DNA testing may one day in the future hold a place in the search. It remains to be seen whether these searches will be desirable, realistic or useful, instead of an over-indulgence with the past, but for adopted people the analysis of DNA may reveal more than they want to know in some scenarios, or deepen the mystery of origins in others.

In reality, and from experience in the genetic clinic, most people at the current time do not have an all-consuming concern or interest in their genome as they go about daily life. There are far too many other preoccupations, especially when financial times are hard and it is enough of a struggle to make ends meet and get the bills paid. Major life events relating to health can, however, suddenly ignite a person's concern about their DNA, genome and genetic risk; an obvious set of such events surrounds starting a family, pregnancy, and the birth of a child with any sort of problem that might have a genetic basis. This is perfectly illustrated by the mother seen in the genetic clinic, herself an adopted person and very healthy, who had no interest in knowing about her birth relatives until she gave birth to a baby with a cleft palate. This case demonstrates very well the interface between adoption and genetic disorders, the information gap, and the dilemmas that frequently arise.

Wherever advances in genetic technologies take us in the future, there will always be a place for a considered, informed, and sometimes cautious approach to the use and interpretation of DNA analysis of an individual's genome. Of equal importance, however, is the documentation and transfer of information relating to health in the adoption process, which is highlighted by the personal stories in this book. It is therefore beholden on those with responsibilities at any point in the adoption process, whether social services or adoptive parents, to have some awareness of the "genetics dimension" for adopted people and their birth relatives, and to know how to access reliable sources of information and professional expertise when required.

SECTION 1

CHAPTER **2**

How genetic disease may pass through the family – patterns of inheritance

Family studies

If we wish to investigate whether a particular trait or disorder in humans is genetic and hereditary, we often depend on the observation of the way in which it is transmitted from one generation to another, or on the study of its frequency among relatives. This may clearly be difficult in adoption scenarios, but the purpose of this section is to help the reader understand the range of possibilities that may be considered by a genetics professional. An important reason for studying the pattern of inheritance of disorders within families is to enable advice to be given to members of a family regarding the likelihood of their developing it or passing it on to their children, i.e. *genetic counselling*. Taking a family history can, in itself, sometimes provide a diagnosis. For example, a child with a fracture after a seemingly trivial injury could come to the attention of a doctor. A family history of relatives with a similar tendency to fracture and blue sclerae (when the "whites" of the eyes appear blue) would suggest the diagnosis of osteogenesis imperfecta (brittle bone disease). In the absence of a positive family history, other diagnoses would have to be considered.

Pedigree drawing and terminology

A pedigree drawing is a shorthand system of recording pertinent information about a family. It usually begins with the person through whom the family came to the attention of the investigator. This person is referred to as the *index* case, *proband* or *propositus*; or, if female, the *proposita*. The position of the proband in the family tree is indicated by an arrow. Information about the health of the rest of the family is obtained by asking direct questions about brothers, sisters, parents, and maternal and paternal relatives, with relevant information about sex, whether affected or not, and relationship to other individuals being carefully recorded in the pedigree chart. Attention to detail can be crucial because the distinction between siblings and *half*-siblings, for example, might be overlooked, or that the child of someone at risk of Huntington's disease is actually a *step*-child and not a birth relative.

There are several ways in which genetic disorders can pass through a family:

- Mendelian inheritance. Inheritance in this way can be autosomal or sex-linked

- Non-mendelian inheritance.

- Mitochondrial inheritance.

These different patterns of inheritance are explained below.

SECTION 1

11

Mendelian inheritance

More than 16,000 traits or disorders in humans exhibit single gene, *unifactorial* or *mendelian inheritance*. This means that a change in the DNA of one gene is overwhelmingly the predominant factor in determining the trait, disorder or disease. However, characteristics such as height, and many common familial disorders, such as diabetes or hypertension, do not usually follow a simple pattern of mendelian inheritance.

A trait or disorder that is determined by a gene on an autosome (a numbered chromosome) is said to show *autosomal inheritance*, whereas a trait or disorder determined by a gene on one of the sex chromosomes is said to show *sex-linked inheritance*.

Autosomal inheritance – dominant

An autosomal dominant trait is one that manifests in the "heterozygous" state, i.e. in a person possessing both an abnormal (mutant) gene copy and the normal copy. It is often possible to trace a dominantly inherited trait or disorder through many generations of a family. In South Africa, for example, the vast majority of cases of a condition called "porphyria variegata", a metabolic disorder exacerbated by sunlight, can be traced back to one couple in the late seventeenth century. This pattern of inheritance is sometimes referred to as "vertical" transmission (not to be confused with "vertical" transmission of infection from mother to child, e.g. of HIV) and is confirmed when male–male (i.e. father to son) transmission is observed (see Figure 1).

Autosomal dominant traits may involve only one organ or part of the body, for example, the eye in congenital cataracts. Alternatively, they may manifest in different systems of the body, and in a variety of ways. The technical word for this is "pleiotropy" – the effects of a single gene giving rise to two or more apparently unrelated effects: for example, tuberous sclerosis, where affected individuals can present with a range of problems including learning difficulties, epilepsy, and a facial skin rash known as adenoma sebaceum.

Figure 1

How a family pedigree might look for a condition following autosomal dominant inheritance. Squares are male and circles female, and filled-in symbols indicate an affected person. The condition can be seen to cross the generations and has been passed from a father to his son, and consequently to his grandson and granddaughter.

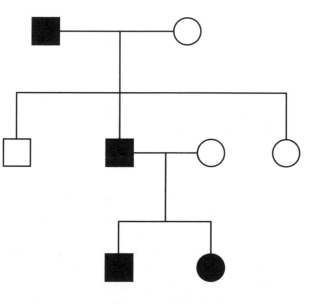

Variable expression

The clinical features of disorders following autosomal dominant inheritance can show striking variation from person to person, even in the same family. This is *variable expression*. In autosomal dominant polycystic kidney disease, for example, some affected individuals may develop renal failure in early adulthood whereas others have just a few kidney cysts that do not affect renal function significantly.

Reduced penetrance

In many autosomal dominant disorders there may be family members who harbour the abnormal gene but show few abnormal clinical features or problems, representing so-called *reduced penetrance*. In common parlance, the disorder "skips a generation". This may be the result of the modifying effects of other genes, as well as interaction of the gene with environmental factors, such as deficiency in certain nutrients. An individual with no features of a disorder, despite having the gene mutation, is said to be *non-penetrant*.

Reduced penetrance, variable expressivity, and pleiotropy all need to be taken into account when trying to interpret family history information for disorders that follow autosomal dominant inheritance.

New mutations

A person affected by an autosomal dominant disorder usually has an affected parent. However, this is not always the case and it may appear in a person when there is no family history of the disorder. A striking example is achondroplasia, a form of short-limbed dwarfism, in which the parents are usually unaffected. The sudden unexpected appearance of a condition like this is due to a *new mutation* having occurred. Prior to genetic testing, the dominant mode of inheritance of achondroplasia could be confirmed only by the observation that the offspring of persons with achondroplasia had a 50 per cent chance of inheriting the condition.

Autosomal inheritance – recessive

Recessive traits and disorders are manifest only when both copies of the gene in question have a mutation or significant variant; this is *homozygosity*. Individuals who are *heterozygous* have just one abnormal copy, are unaffected and perfectly healthy; they are therefore described as *carriers*. An autosomal recessive trait or disorder, in contrast to dominant inheritance, will usually be seen only in full siblings – brothers and sisters. This is sometimes referred to as "horizontal" transmission, but this is misleading.

Consanguinity

Enquiry into the family history of individuals affected with rare recessive traits or disorders might reveal that their parents are related, i.e. *consanguineous*. In the case of a very rare recessive disorder, it is more likely that the parents are consanguineous. For cystic fibrosis, however, which is the most common "serious" autosomal recessive disorder found in Western Europeans, the frequency of parental consanguinity is only slightly greater than that seen in the general population. In large inbred family communities, where cousin marriage is quite normal, an autosomal recessive condition may well be present in more than one branch of the family. This applies to certain immigrant groups in the UK and, for example, Traveller communities.

Genetic risks

The risk of a child inheriting both abnormal copies of a gene from unaffected carrier parents, and thus being *affected*, is 1 in 4, or 25 per cent (see Figure 2). Where only one parent is a carrier of a particular gene fault, the chance of the offspring being a carrier, but *unaffected*, is 1 in 2, or 50 per cent. In inbred family communities or groups, it may be observed that a recessively inherited condition is passed from an affected parent to a child. This occurs because the unaffected parent is a carrier of the same

15

condition, and in this situation the risk to the offspring is 1 in 2 (50 per cent). This is referred to as *pseudodominant* inheritance.

Figure 2

In autosomal recessive inheritance, the parents (grey circle and square), of an affected child (black square) are both healthy carriers of the condition. The chances of having an affected child in each pregnancy is 1 in 4, or 25 per cent. The offspring of the affected person will not all be carriers. The condition is nearly always confined to one generation of siblings.

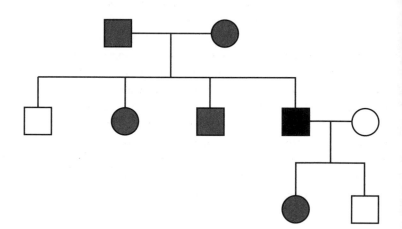

Sex-linked inheritance

"Sex-linked" refers to the pattern of inheritance seen when conditions are caused by faulty or mutated genes that are located on either of the sex chromosomes. Genes carried on the X chromosome are referred to as being *X-linked*. Those carried on the Y chromosome are referred to as exhibiting *Y-linked* or *holandric inheritance*; however, in practice the latter are very unusual because if there is anything wrong with the Y chromosome, the man is usually infertile as sperm production is seriously impaired. Only males are affected by the rare conditions due to faulty Y chromosome genes and only male–male (father to son) transmission is observed.

X-linked recessive inheritance

Conditions or traits following X-linked recessive inheritance are usually seen only in males. Such conditions can be transmitted through a family by healthy female carriers to affected males. If and when these men have children of their own, their daughters will be carriers of the condition. An X-linked condition cannot be passed from a father to his son. It is also possible, indeed in some X-linked conditions it is common, for X-linked recessive conditions to suddenly occur without a family history being present. This is due to a new mutation (as sometimes occurs in dominantly inherited conditions).

We have been aware of X-linked inheritance for a long time. This was understood and appreciated by the Jewish community nearly 2,000 years ago in relation to haemophilia. The sons of all the sisters of a mother who had sons with the "bleeding disease" were excused from circumcision. Conversely, the sons of her husband's sisters were not excused. Queen Victoria was a carrier of haemophilia, and her carrier daughters, who were perfectly healthy, introduced the gene into the Russian and Spanish royal families. Fortunately for the British royal family, Queen Victoria's son, Edward VII, did not inherit the gene, and so could not transmit it to his descendants.

Genetic risks

For a carrier female of an X-linked recessive disorder, each son has a 1 in 2, or 50 per cent, chance of being affected, and each daughter also has a 1 in 2 chance of being a carrier (see Figure 3). For some X-linked diseases, for example, Duchenne muscular dystrophy, the condition is usually so severe that the affected boys do not grow up to reproduce – they normally deteriorate, weaken, and die at around 20–25 years of age. They do not therefore transmit the disease to carrier daughters, with the potential to be transmitted to sons in the next generation, so cases occur in families either because of a new mutation in a carrier female or in an affected boy.

Figure 3

In X-linked recessive inheritance, the chance of a carrier female (grey circle) having an affected son (black square) is 1 in 4, although if the sex of the foetus is known to be male, the chance is 1 in 2. For the offspring of the affected male, all girls will be obligate carriers but the sons will be unaffected.

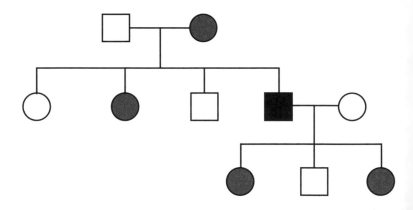

Manifestation of X-linked diseases in carrier females

It is not unusual for the carrier females of X-linked recessive diseases to have some mild manifestations of the condition in question. Carriers of haemophilia, for example, may have a mildly deranged blood-clotting condition. This may be important in making a diagnosis in a female child for adoption if the family history information is unavailable or sketchy.

A female might also manifest an X-linked recessive disorder by being a carrier of an X-linked recessive mutation and having only a single X chromosome, which is the situation in Turner syndrome. Women with Turner syndrome have problems, including short stature, a form of congenital heart disease and infertility. It can usually be easily diagnosed through a standard chromosome test.

X-linked dominant inheritance

Although rare, some X-linked disorders are manifest in the heterozygous female to a similar degree as seen in the male who has the mutant gene on his single X chromosome. This is known as X-linked dominant inheritance. The condition may track through the family in a pattern resembling dominant inheritance but with the important difference that a man cannot pass the condition to his son. Examples include an inherited form of rickets and a form of hereditary neuropathy (a nerve condition).

Some X-linked dominant conditions are only seen in girls because if the mutation occurs in males (with only one X chromosome), the effects are so severe that a miscarriage usually occurs. Examples of these conditions include Rett syndrome (severe learning difficulties and epilepsy) and incontinentia pigmenti (a skin condition).

Non-mendelian inheritance

Sex influence

Some hereditary problems and traits that basically follow
dominant inheritance occur more frequently in one sex than
in another, which is so-called *sex influence*. Some of this relates
to hormonal differences, for example, male pattern baldness.
Congenital dysplasia (abnormal development) of the hip occurs
more commonly in girls, but when it occurs in a boy the risk of his
offspring also being affected is higher than the risk to the offspring
of an affected female. Sex influence should not be confused with
sex-linked (X-linked) inheritance.

Inheritance patterns involving more than one gene

The traditional approach to understanding genetic disease has
centred on chromosome abnormalities as well as single gene
(mendelian) inheritance. Thus far, the main patterns of inheritance
have been outlined but the main chromosomal conditions, such
as Down syndrome (an extra chromosome 21) and those with an
extra X chromosome – Klinefelter syndrome in boys and Triple X
syndrome in girls – have not been discussed.

Increasingly, we are learning how more than one gene variant,
sometimes several, are responsible for determining medical
problems. These are *complex* traits and are transmitted through a
family in a less clear-cut way compared to mendelian conditions.
Furthermore, environmental factors may be important. In spina
bifida, for example, a genetic predisposition interacts with partial
deficiency of folic acid to cause a problem that can be devastating.
When a woman takes additional folic acid supplements in her
diet throughout the time when she conceives, and during the first
few weeks of pregnancy, the risk of spina bifida is much reduced,
although not abolished completely. Whether or not a problem
manifests is also likely to depend on the combination of gene

variants inherited from both parents. Many cases of autism probably fall into this category, which is why it has been slow to yield its genetic secrets, and there is much for us still to learn.

Digenic inheritance

Digenic inheritance could be thought of as the simplest form of complex trait. It refers to a disorder due to the additive effects of mutations at two different locations of the gene map. Several examples are now well known to geneticists, but the most important group of problems is the inherited cardiomyopathies, which can cause sudden premature death because the heart stops. These conditions are not rare and could easily be a concern in adoption scenarios, for example, if there is a history of sudden premature death in a close biological relative with no further information being available (see the case study in Chapter 4).

Anticipation

There are some disorders following autosomal dominant inheritance where the onset of the disease occurs at an earlier age in the offspring than in the parents, which continues over several generations, and the general severity of problems in each generation is also worse. This phenomenon is called *anticipation* and is relevant in adoption because of the diseases in which it is a factor. These include Huntington's disease which, because of the devastating effect it has on the individual and family life, is not infrequently encountered in adoption scenarios. Other conditions are myotonic dystrophy (a form of muscular dystrophy with cataracts and a variety of other problems) and fragile-X syndrome (a learning difficulty condition following X-linked inheritance) which, again because of the impact they can have on family life, may be encountered in children who come into the care system.

Mosaicism

It is not unusual for an individual to have more than one cell type, due to a gene variant or mutation occurring at any stage after

SECTION 1

conception; this is known as *mosaicism*. It might involve a whole chromosome (e.g. mosaic Down syndrome where the child has an extra chromosome number 21 in some tissues but not all). In general, the phenomenon is very common – for example, all those skin "moles" or permanent blemishes that we have are due to gene variants occurring in a small clump of cells, giving rise to a different growth pattern and pigment change. Most of these changes don't matter but cancer can be thought of as a form of mosaicism because a range of genetic changes have occurred to cause cell growth in a particular tissue to reach an uncontrolled state – hence tumours that enlarge and spread.

A specific form of mosaicism sometimes occurs in the tissues making eggs or sperm, i.e. the *gonads* – testis and ovary. The recurrence of a particular gene mutation in this tissue alone can account for normal parents having a second affected child for a condition that is not expected to recur, but the risk of this happening is low. However, it has to be taken into consideration during genetic counselling for some conditions. This is known as *germline*, or *gonadal*, mosaicism.

Mitochondrial inheritance

There is a group of important medical conditions that occur because of a change in the DNA that is found in the *mitochondria* of the cell. Each cell contains thousands of mitochondria, which can be thought of as power stations, or batteries, of a cell because they generate energy. They have their own small stretch of DNA into which is written the specific code of a relatively small number of genes. An error in one of these genes may lead to faulty energy production, which can manifest as muscle fatigue and a great variety of other problems, e.g. affecting the heart, hearing, or causing diabetes. The effects can be very variable in an individual. Importantly, we all inherit mitochondrial DNA from our mother.

In a family pedigree that charts a mitochondrial disease, it will be observed that both males and females can be affected but the condition is never passed on by an affected man to his offspring. This is called *matrilinear* inheritance (see Figure 4). One unfortunate possibility is that the risk to the children born to a mildly affected mother (who may not have been given a diagnosis) may approach 100 per cent. Clearly, this particular pattern may be relevant to adoption where the mother's condition progresses to the point where she becomes too unwell to look after her children and all are at risk of developing the same condition.

Figure 4

A pedigree demonstrating mitochondrial inheritance might look like that shown below. Affected individuals (black symbols) only inherit the condition from their mother; some individuals (grey symbols) may be very mildly affected and difficult to diagnose. These conditions cannot pass from affected males to their offspring.

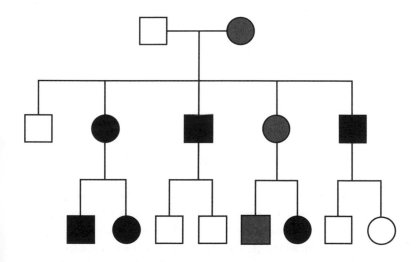

Genomic imprinting

In genetics, it is now recognised that when a gene fault is passed on to a child, quite different clinical problems can result, depending on whether the gene is inherited from the father or from the mother. This is referred to as a "parent of origin" effect, or *genomic imprinting*. The best-known examples of childhood conditions, where the imprinting has gone wrong, are Prader-Willi (PWS) and Angelman syndromes (AS). Defective DNA on chromosome 15 can reach the child but the effects are very different according to whether the defect has occurred on the father's copy of chromosome 15 (PWS) or the mother's copy (AS). PWS and AS are both learning difficulty conditions (severe in AS) but children with PWS tend to overeat and be underactive, whilst children with AS tend to have a lot of energy and may develop epilepsy. On chromosome 11, there is a complex region of DNA where different disruptions to the imprinting mechanism give rise to an overgrowth condition (Beckwith-Wiedemann syndrome) or a small stature condition (Russell-Silver syndrome), depending on whether the mother's or father's copy is involved. There are many other general effects of imprinting and we are beginning to learn a lot more about these in relation to health and disease.

The importance of a genetic diagnosis and establishing the mode of inheritance

For you as adoptive parents or carers, it is very important to know whether a medical or developmental problem has a genetic basis. Making a diagnosis may not, by itself, change a great deal, particularly if it is a learning difficulty problem. However, simply to establish the reason for a problem is beneficial because a line can then be drawn under the efforts that have been made to reach a diagnosis, and those efforts are often lengthy, costly and distressing.

A diagnosis may assist the process of securing support for your child at school, for example, through a Statement of Educational Needs – it is striking how often parents testify to the difference that a firm diagnosis makes.

Parallel to a genetic diagnosis is the information that goes with it in terms of the pattern, or potential pattern, of inheritance. Whilst perhaps not the most immediate concern when a child is placed for fostering or adoption, it may be crucial to the various parties as your child grows up.

- Your child will one day be an adult who may wish to have children – will he or she be given any information about genetic risks relating to their own problem?

- If the genetic problem was not diagnosed before your adopted child was removed from his or her birth parents, will the information about your child's health, and the genetic risk to any other children they might have, reach those birth parents?

- Suppose a known genetic problem affects one or both of your adopted child's birth parents – how will this information reach your child so that he or she is aware of any future genetic risk?

- And then there are the siblings of your adopted child – will they benefit from any relevant information about genetic risk following a diagnosis regarding the adopted child?

- Or, if a birth sibling develops a genetic problem and a diagnosis is made, will the information reach your adopted child in advance of him or her wanting to start a family?

- How do you, as adoptive parents, deal with the weight

SECTION I

of responsibility of having to pass on genetic information appropriately to your adopted child?

These questions inevitably raise important issues, not only about the efforts that are made to secure a diagnosis when a genetic condition is suspected, but also about the documentation and preservation of information, and how it flows through the system and between agencies for the benefit of the adopted child, and others.

CHAPTER 3

When a child has a known or suspected genetic disease

How common are genetic diseases?

In general, when health care professionals think of "genetic disease", they have in mind "rare conditions", and this would apply to most of the public as well. Increasingly, however, the genetic basis of many "common", or commoner, medical problems is being unravelled, for example, susceptibility to asthma, eczema or diabetes mellitus. For diabetes, we are learning that there are many different genetic varieties, though the most common "insulin-dependent" form should not be thought of as being "strongly" genetic. The risk of this form of diabetes occurring in first degree relatives is higher than the background risk to the general population but it is not as high as the risk for mendelian genetic disease. Some rare forms of diabetes, however, do carry mendelian genetic risks because alterations in a single gene are the most significant causative factor.

But "rare conditions", which are usually what we are dealing with in considering genetic disease, should be considered in context. Although there are thousands of rare disorders, when all lumped together they are surprisingly common. One in 17 people will have a disease classed as rare during their lifetime, and most of these are conditions with a strong or significant genetic basis. Therefore many people live with, and cope with, a medical problem or disease with a genetic basis, and it follows that the population of adopted children, their birth parents, and of course their adoptive parents, are no different from everyone else in this respect.

Inheriting a genetic disease

Some genetic conditions do not have hereditary implications, largely because the affected individual is unlikely to have their own children, either for social reasons, or in cases of severe learning disability, or because the condition might be associated with infertility, or because the problem is severely life-limiting with death occurring before adulthood.

A good example to consider is Down syndrome, which most people know is due to an extra chromosome (number 21) making 47 chromosomes in all (rather than the normal 46). Clearly, this is a "genetic" condition, but only rarely is it a condition with hereditary implications. Most cases occur as "one-off" medical genetic events in a family, and persons with Down syndrome are very unlikely to have children of their own, although it may be biologically possible and does happen on rare occasions. When it does happen, there is a genetic risk that the child will have Down syndrome as well. Interestingly, this is not true for some of the other disorders where the total number of chromosomes is abnormal. In Klinefelter syndrome, where males have an extra X chromosome (resulting in above average height, a slightly female body shape, and very mild speech delay), the condition virtually always confers infertility (sometimes these men are diagnosed when investigations are carried out by an infertility clinic), and this is also true for Turner syndrome, where females have only one X chromosome (making 45 instead of 46 in all).

There are two "whole chromosome" conditions (called *aneuploidies*), that are perfectly consistent with normal fertility. One affects males who have an extra Y chromosome. They are fertile men and there is no extra risk of an extra Y chromosome arising in their offspring. The other affects females who have an extra X chromosome – often referred to as "Triple X" syndrome. These women are often of above-average height and very slim, they are fertile, and there is no increased risk of major chromosome problems in the offspring. These last two conditions are associated with mild educational and behavioural problems, so for adopted children displaying problems of this kind, and there will be many, a chromosome test should be considered. It may reveal a very tangible reason for the problems rather than ascribing blame to background and nurturing.

The author recently made a diagnosis of Triple X syndrome in an older teenager who had left her adoptive home to live with her partner. Throughout childhood and growing up in the adoptive home, there had been a history of poor educational achievement but she had never had any genetic investigations; in the end the chromosome test was undertaken because she suffered repeated miscarriages.

The role of patient support groups

It will be appreciated by the reader that this short book cannot possibly attempt to be a medical genetic textbook that provides detailed information about even the more common genetic conditions – and there are simply too many rare genetic diseases to list here. But there are many other good sources of information. It is quite normal these days for patients, or parents, to read about their condition or the condition affecting their child through an internet search. This can sometimes work quite well, but information on the internet is not always verified and may not be presented in a format that is helpful for a specific situation. Some caution and discernment is therefore needed.

There are many patient support groups which have been set up to provide information for new patients, to bring patients and families together, and to share experiences. The organisation Contact a Family can be a very useful resource in finding the right support group and appropriate information (see Useful Organisations).

Whilst many of these groups have recognised expert medical advisers, they are run by the members themselves. Some are very structured and committed to keeping up to date, often organising conferences and providing opportunities for affected patients and families to meet each other if they wish. The very well organised groups support patients and families in need, and often successfully raise funds, even contributing significantly to the work of scientific research into a specific condition.

Most, if not all, patient groups now have their own websites. The information given on these may meet patients' needs but, here again, some caution is required. Sometimes a website portrays a condition in a way that is rather dramatic and eye-catching compared to the real situation faced by a patient. It is not unusual in the genetic clinic to hear people say that they were shocked by what they read on a patient support website because it described "worst case scenarios" for their diagnosis, which do not necessarily apply to them. Most conditions are very variable in their severity, and this is not always appreciated until it is carefully explained by a professional.

The challenge of "genetics" to traditional medical ethics

So, although this book is not attempting to provide all the medical and scientific answers pertaining to a specific diagnosis, it is important to lay out some principles about the clinical genetic approach to medical problems as they affect the adoption process and, most importantly, the adopted child. The clinical geneticist's approach to a medical problem with a genetic basis is slightly different to a routine medical approach.

- In the traditional medical model, the patient with a symptom is dealt with on an individual basis and the investigations are carried out on that individual alone. Strict rules of patient confidentiality, disclosure and non-disclosure of information, and autonomy, apply, according to conventionally accepted principles of medical ethics.

- However, in the realm of genetic conditions and hereditary disease, there is often a clash or conflict with these very good ethical principles. The reason is, of course, that all of us *share* our genetic make-up with our biological relatives.

For all of us, our genetic make-up is essentially composed of a 50 per cent contribution from our mothers and a 50 per cent contribution from our fathers. We have no choice about the content of this genetic make-up, though it is possible for the parents, in circumstances relating to genetic risk problems, to make a choice; I refer of course to pre-natal testing, which might result in selective termination of pregnancy, or embryo selection on the basis of genetic testing combined with in-vitro fertilisation (IVF).

The fact that we share our genetic make-up with our relatives therefore confronts, and may conflict with, the usual principles of medical ethics. In clinical genetics we consider the "true patient" to be "the family" rather than the individual, although this is not to diminish the importance of the affected individual, who may have symptoms, and for whom treatment is paramount. In the context of the adoption process and adopted children, therefore, it can be very difficult to practise ideal clinical genetics because of family disruption.

The child with a known diagnosis

As far as your adopted child is concerned, there will not be any significant medical differences in looking after him or her compared to a birth family situation. Take a child with a diagnosis of cystic fibrosis, for example. The adoptive parents have the challenging task of looking after their child who will very likely have chronic health problems affecting mainly the chest, as well as digestion, but they are unlikely to be thinking of "the genes" as they battle with the child's various illnesses, hospital admissions, constant antibiotic treatment, and many other issues. So this is no different to the task facing birth parents – they face exactly the same challenges with a child who has cystic fibrosis.

Whether you as adoptive parents, at a deeper level, can detach yourselves from "the genetics" of the situation is an interesting issue to speculate upon. The birth parents of a child with cystic fibrosis may naturally feel a sense of guilt, and blame themselves for their child's severe health condition and the suffering he or she is experiencing. After all, the illness has occurred due to the faulty genes passed on to the child by them – 'It's all our fault!' is an understandable reaction and not uncommon (grandparents often experience this sense of guilt too). Adoptive parents, by contrast, have no logical reason to harbour feelings of guilt and self-blame;

in fact, they may be affirmed in their role because they feel they have rescued the child from a situation where the care might have been sub-optimal compared to that which they are providing.

If your child has cystic fibrosis, or any other diagnosed condition, you and everyone else involved knows what they are dealing with – certain problems can be anticipated and it will largely be true that "to be forewarned is to be forearmed". This is very well illustrated in the personal story about Taylor in Section II of this book. Everything became easier to cope with once a diagnosis had been made that explained her short stature. With the uncertainties removed, it was possible to move on and deal with the problems at hand. For many children, however, the uncertainties about a diagnosis will not be easily resolved and the search for answers may go on. Nowhere is this more true than for children with some unspecified developmental delay or learning disability, and this is the most common reason for the local paediatrician, who is dealing with the adoption placement, to seek help from the regional clinical genetics service, often asking for the child to be seen and assessed as soon as possible.

The role of the clinical geneticist

Many people have the notion that a clinical geneticist is a doctor who only undertakes research into genetic conditions. Most clinical geneticists, however, have no salaried research time and their job is to see patients and families. Referrals to a geneticist include people across the entire age range, from infancy to old age; in fact, even beyond that because there is often a need to track down information from a death certificate or post-mortem examination, or even from samples stored in a pathology laboratory if it is deemed helpful to conduct a DNA test on a deceased person. The role of clinical geneticist can be summed up by saying that the service deals with anyone who has, or is at

risk of, a diagnosis, or possible diagnosis, of a genetic condition
or disease. The specific expertise centres around understanding
genetics, and human genetics in particular, knowing a lot about
rare genetic diseases, being able to appropriately investigate
patients and families through genetic tests, and to interpret the
results.

However, despite rapidly advancing laboratory technologies,
genetic testing does not always yield an answer, and therefore
a diagnosis. This may of course be because the child, or patient,
does not have a condition with a genetic basis, but is also quite
likely to be due to the limitations of the genetic tests available
at any given time; there is still much to learn and discover in
this field. That is why the geneticist will often say that we don't
know the answer now but it is quite possible that a better test
will be available when the child grows up, or in 10 years' time
perhaps. For many years, from the late 1950s, the standard form
of genetic test available was looking down a microscope at
chromosomes to see if they appeared normal. It later became
possible with "banding" techniques to see chromosomes as
structures looking like bar codes, and therefore to see small
defects more easily. From the 1980s onwards, the number of
tests that could be performed based on DNA analysis increased
steadily but the geneticist could only request a specific genetic
test once a specific genetic condition was suspected. In other
words, these DNA-based tests did not, and still do not, provide
a complete view of the genetic material. But in the last 10 years
significant revolutions have taken place in genetic testing which
have transformed, and will continue to transform, the whole
landscape of investigation for genetic disease. Tests carried out
using the new technology (referred to as "next-generation
sequencing"(NGS)) are rapidly becoming routine.

CASE STUDY

A two-year-old girl was referred to the clinical genetics service by a paediatrician. She demonstrated some developmental and speech delay and had a head size at the bottom of the normal range. She had been fostered from 15 months of age and adopted at 19 months; her birth parents had mild learning difficulties themselves and were unable to cope with the challenges of a baby. The clinical geneticist examined the child and obtained as much information as possible about the medical history of the birth family. The birth parents were still together, living in the region, had no other children at that time, and had letterbox contact with their daughter. No specific syndrome or reason for the child's developmental delay could be ascertained and a standard chromosome test proved normal.

The child was followed up and, by the time she was seven, it was clear that she had mild but definite global developmental delay, as well as a small head size as previously noted when examined at the age of two. The result of a blood test about six weeks later showed that the girl had a small but possibly significant duplication on part of chromosome 15, but this was not an abnormality known to be associated with a specific range of clinical problems. However, it was a sufficiently large duplication to suggest a strong likelihood of being clinically significant; further investigation was therefore warranted if at all possible.

The adoptive parents were informed of the result and they requested social services to make every effort to contact the birth parents. Two years later, the birth parents were seen by the same geneticist in another clinic in the region, and the situation was explained with appropriate care and discretion. It emerged that the birth father had been seen by the genetics service some years earlier as a boy, because of mild learning difficulties, together with his brother and mother. The brother had more severe learning difficulties and their mother had a history of educational difficulties as well, and was described as "backward". The birth mother had been removed from her own birth parents as a child because of violence and abuse, and she thought both her parents had mild learning difficulties. There had been no contact with them for a long time. She had one full sister, who had two sons, and five maternal half-sisters, but there had been no contact with any of them for years.

The birth parents were offered a test to look for the same duplicated segment of chromosome found in their child who had been adopted, and this showed the father's result to be normal whilst the mother also had the chromosome 15 duplication. When this was explained to them they declared that they had no plans to have more children. The chromosome 15 abnormality was designated as an inherited microduplication in the biological family and suspicions about its pathogenicity (capability to cause an abnormal condition) were heightened but not proven. After all, the father also had a personal family history of mild learning problems. It was therefore theoretically possible that the adopted daughter had inherited an undetected genetic fault from his side also, which could be either the true cause of her developmental delay (i.e. nothing to do with the chromosome 15 finding), or perhaps contributing to it.

Two months later the birth parents were seen again in the genetic clinic because the birth mother was pregnant (despite having said that they had no plans to have more children). Social services were informed of the situation.

The birth parents were seen again nine months later with their new baby daughter and the baby's foster carer (the plan for the child was adoption). The baby had been diagnosed with growth retardation in the womb; it was alleged that there had been no drinking or smoking during pregnancy. Following discussion, a decision was made to test the baby for the chromosome 15 duplication. The result came back positive, and this will be an important topic to be discussed when prospective adoptive parents are found. However, there is still uncertainty about what it might mean for both children's futures. Both of the girls, either fostered or adopted, will be candidates for genetic counselling when they are older, i.e. probably in their early teenage years.

This case illustrates how much clinical work was required with the birth family in order to try and accurately interpret the micro-array findings.

The future of genetic testing

Enormous progress has occurred in genetic technologies over the last 20 years. It is only a matter of time before the complete sequencing, letter by letter, of the DNA that comprises the genome or exome becomes possible. Analyses using next-generation sequencing (NGS) are already well established in a research setting and have been strikingly successful in the identification of the genetic cause of very rare conditions that could not otherwise easily be investigated using older systems and technologies.

Whilst geneticists will in time sequence even more of the genome, it is still likely that parental DNA will have to be analysed alongside that of a child in order for a meaningful interpretation to be possible. Therefore, these new technologies will pose the same sort of challenges to the adoption process when genetic testing is being undertaken prior to placement (and even after placement) with a view to trying to establish a diagnosis.

CHAPTER 4

When a child's birth parents, or other biological relatives, develop, or may develop, a genetic disease

For your adopted child to benefit from genetic testing in the same way as children looked after by their birth parents, you will have to consider the situation post-placement (perhaps many years post-placement) if one of your child's birth parents develops a medical condition that may have hereditary implications for their birth children. This may not have been known when your child was placed with you and is therefore new information. However, there may be significant challenges relating to the decision to convey the information to your adopted child and/or to you, as well as logistical difficulties in doing so. Furthermore, where does the responsibility for the transfer of information lie?

In a usual situation the clinical geneticist, or other doctor, would discuss with the family how best to inform other relatives about a medical condition with actual or potential hereditary implications. Families usually find a way to disseminate the information appropriately, and sometimes the doctor will write a "To whom it may concern" letter, which the patient can then send to family members deemed to be at risk of the genetic condition. Of course, sometimes families have split up, either geographically or acrimoniously, so that contacting the "at risk" relatives is impossible, or at least very difficult. In some circumstances, where the genetic risk information could be vital for a birth relative's health or decision to have children, the geneticist will take it upon themselves to try and feed the information to the relatives, if their whereabouts can be determined. This might also involve the family doctor/GP. Whilst this may be viewed as breaching patient confidentiality, it is a special situation in medical ethics where the doctor is acting in the best interests of the person at risk, and it is entirely defendable. Indeed, there are a number of expert working party reports that make these points, including those from the Nuffield Council of Bio-ethics (http://nuffieldbioethics. org and search for "genetic screening" – the 1993 report and 2006 supplement are both of interest).

This situation arises because there are many genetic, hereditary conditions that do not become apparent until adult life, and sometimes until middle age and beyond. Broad groups of conditions include neurological disorders such as neuropathies (diseases of the nervous system causing weakness and numbness); hereditary forms of Parkinson's disease or motor neurone disease; some forms of muscular dystrophy; cardiomyopathies, which may present with sudden death at almost any time in adult life (sometimes earlier); the inherited disorders of heart rhythm (cardiac arrhythmias); and various strongly inherited cancer syndromes. Many of these conditions demonstrate autosomal dominant inheritance, which means that any biological offspring are at 50 per cent risk of inheriting the condition, even though there may have been no apparent health problems or symptoms at the time when a child was conceived and born.

The problems posed by this situation in adoption can be illustrated by the following case studies. These are based on real cases from the genetics clinic, modified to avoid identifying details.

CASE STUDY I

A 34-year-old woman was referred to the genetic clinic because she had become aware of shoulder and upper limb weakness over a five-year period, for example, when lifting items off a shelf in the kitchen or brushing her hair. She was also aware of a cousin having some muscular weakness problems but no further details were available. When examined, she had demonstrable upper limb weakness, weakness of her shoulder muscles and upper leg muscles, as well as facial muscles – she could not whistle, grimace, or puff out her cheeks. A clinical diagnosis of facio-scapulo-humeral muscular dystrophy (FSHD) was made, and this was subsequently confirmed on genetic testing, which at the time had only recently been introduced for the condition. It emerged during the initial consultation that she had given birth to a baby girl who would now be 10 years old. She had been conceived as the result of a brief liaison and had been adopted. There was no contact of any kind with her.

FSHD is a muscular dystrophy that follows autosomal dominant inheritance and the daughter who had been adopted was therefore conceived at 50 per cent risk of inheriting the condition. As there was no contact with the adopted daughter or her adoptive family, the geneticist wrote to the adoption agency and explained the situation. The agency replied that the adoptive family lived in another part of the region and their whereabouts were known. The adoption agency forwarded a letter detailing information about FSHD, written by the geneticist, to the adoptive parents.

Eventually, seven years later, the adopted daughter's GP contacted the genetics service about her. She had reached the age of 17 and wanted to talk about the condition and her own situation. She was seen and, as it happened, assessed in the clinic, by the same geneticist who had dealt with her birth mother. There was some indication, although only a slight one, that she might have some subtle weakness but, clinically, it was not possible to be sure. It was decided to see her again two years later.

When she returned to the clinic the situation was largely unchanged; she was functioning well and going about her normal daily tasks, including some physical activity. It was considered possible that she might have subtle facial weakness but she decided the time had come to request predictive genetic testing for FSHD. The result was positive and she was therefore seen again to discuss the condition and implications for having children herself.

This particular case can be considered successful because a way was found to alert and inform the adoptive parents of the birth mother's diagnosis, and the risk of the adopted daughter developing FSHD at some point in the future. It was handled sensitively by all parties involved, so that when a diagnosis was eventually made, the adopted daughter was well prepared for the issues. She had been able to come to terms with the risk over a period of time so that, when she asked to have a predictive test, she was sure of her decision and could accept the outcome. The result means that she has to consider what sort of career is possible for her, and she knows the risk to her future offspring, should she wish to have children. It would be theoretically possible to ask for pre-implantation diagnosis (PGD) with IVF in order to avoid having an affected child.

CASE STUDY 2

Some 15 years after a child had been adopted in early childhood, the brother of the birth father developed symptoms of fatigue and shortness of breath on exertion. On investigation he was found to have a form of cardiomyopathy (heart muscle weakness) combined with a disturbance of heart rhythm. He was treated by a cardiologist and some improvement in symptoms took place. It was known that a maternal uncle had dropped dead suddenly at work around the age of 50. The birth father asked to be investigated and a heart scan revealed some mild, but probably significant, changes in his heart muscle thickness; he had also experienced a couple of episodes of fainting without obvious reason. There was some minor disturbance to his heart rhythm and he was told that he should have an intra-cardiac device (ICD) fitted in case he one day developed a seriously irregular heart rhythm that could be life-threatening.

Since he had a very brief relationship with the birth mother years ago, he had no further contact with her but knew that she had a child who had been adopted. He never told his wife and children about what took place but, having now been told that he had a hereditary heart condition, he wondered what he should do.

The medical problem that has emerged in the birth father, his brother, and in the history of his maternal uncle, clearly indicates a hereditary heart condition. There are many different forms of cardiomyopathy but the majority are genetic, so the adopted child was conceived at 50 per cent risk and is now aged 16. She should start screening for cardiomyopathy because, like her birth father, she might need an ICD fitted to prevent a life-threatening upset to her heart rhythm.

This type of condition is one of the main reasons why some young athletes, on rare occasions, die suddenly on a sports field. This birth father knows nothing about his birth child but, for all he knows, she might be an athlete at increased risk of sudden death as a young adult. Furthermore, he has kept that part of his personal life secret from his partner, with whom he has children who are also at risk of cardiomyopathy.

It is clearly in the best interests of the adopted child that relevant information is passed on so that she can have the opportunity to benefit from appropriate screening investigations for cardiomyopathy. This might, literally, be life-saving if she has inherited the condition but has not yet shown any symptoms. If the information can be given to her, it will probably come as a shock to learn that she is at risk of a potentially serious medical condition that was not suspected when she was adopted. The situation presents a number of very sensitive challenges that involve confidentiality and breaking bad news.

It is important to appreciate that a scenario similar to this could also occur in relation to strongly inherited forms of common cancer, such as breast or bowel cancer. Whilst there would not be the same urgency for screening in the young adopted person, the information is nevertheless just as important for her as life goes on, and if she contemplates having a family of her own.

CASE STUDY 3

An adoption social worker, with the approval of the medical adviser, contacted the regional clinical genetics service with an urgent request. They had an eight-month-old baby who was going to be adopted by very suitable prospective adoptive parents, and wanted to proceed as quickly as possible. The baby girl was slightly small in length, at the very bottom of the normal length/height range. She was otherwise healthy with normal development and was being placed for adoption because of abuse by the birth parents, with whom no contact can be allowed. The child had an older brother whose height is average. There is a slightly distant, but strong, family history of some form of "dwarfism", although the exact diagnosis is not known. The prospective adoptive parents asked for firm guarantees that the baby, who is short, will not go on to develop "dwarfism"; hence the referral to clinical genetics.

The pattern of "dwarfism" in one branch of the family is documented by the social worker as "clearly inherited". The problems regarding this information are two-fold:

45

firstly, no specific diagnosis has been provided to the geneticist and, secondly, the term "dwarfism" means different things to different people. Are the affected individuals simply short compared to most people or do they have a condition with very short stature, i.e. a "dwarfing" syndrome (it should be noted that the term "dwarf" is no longer used in a medical context). This is a classic situation where the geneticist needs accurate information to deal with the request but the possibility of obtaining it is poor because the birth parents are not co-operative. The geneticist would wish to examine them, to know their heights, and the heights of the relatives who are the link to that part of the family said to have "dwarfism".

The geneticist can, of course, examine the child being placed for adoption, as requested, but how far can this go in reassuring the prospective adoptive parents? Is this a case where, in order to provide a prognosis for the child, a range of genetic tests could be undertaken to see if there is a mutation or variant in a gene that is known to cause short stature? How many such tests should be considered? In the foreseeable future, it will be possible to sequence all the genes in one analysis (whole exome sequencing), so should this be done to try and resolve the issue? But to conduct such a test would mean that other, unexpected, genetic variants or mutations might be identified, and their interpretation could be thwarted because no access to the birth parents is possible.

These questions are very unlikely to arise if the child were not being placed for adoption. The history and information available would probably be much clearer and the geneticist's assessment much easier. Given the information as it stands, it is unlikely that a child whose stature is at the bottom of the normal population range, but who is otherwise developing normally, would be subjected to a large battery of genetic tests. The approach would more likely be to follow the child over a period of time, measure growth and assess development, and only investigate further if it is clearly justified on clinical grounds.

In this scenario, the adoptive parents can be given substantial reassurance about the child's future if there are no unusual features to suggest a known short stature syndrome. However, it would not be possible to give *total* reassurance, because no absolute guarantee can be given regarding the future, and in this case the information on which to base a medical opinion is lacking. So, to what extent is it reasonable for prospective adoptive parents to query "conditions" of this nature?

In all these case studies, the central issue has been the welfare of the adopted child and the hope that their health, and potential health risks, are not seriously compromised because they have been separated from their birth family. In Case Study 1, the information was transmitted successfully and sensitively with a good outcome in terms of *process*. The other cases present greater and different challenges that are less easy to resolve. Naturally, similar challenges are encountered in families where there is no issue relating to adoption, but all parties involved in the adoption process have a duty of care towards the child.

At key stages in the process, therefore, documentation of good quality information is paramount in order that the child may benefit from medical screening in the same way as anyone living in a birth family, where there is no major obstruction to the flow of information. Case Study 3 also highlights the issue of whether some form of genetic testing should be undertaken on an eight-month-old child that would normally not be contemplated if the child was being brought up by their birth parents. Familiarity with the Practice Note *Genetic Testing and Adoption* (BAAF, 2006) would help health care workers and social workers with their roles in such cases.

The issue of genetic testing in children, and whether adoption presents a special situation, is further discussed in the next chapter.

CHAPTER 5

Genetic testing of children – special issues in adoption?

To test or not to test?

Where genetic tests are usually very different from other tests is in their capacity to uncover information about a child's *future* health expectations in the medium or long term, as opposed to dealing with acute or present-day health issues and problems. The question that clearly arises is whether, and/or when, it is in the best interests of your child to undergo a genetic test if there are no obvious benefits *to your child* in the immediate or short term. One cannot expect young children to understand the reason for a test of this nature and, if there are no immediate or short-term benefits, your child should not be denied the opportunity of making the decision independently for himself or herself. In other words, they cannot make the choice later "not to be tested" if this option has been removed. It might also be the case that you, as adoptive parents or carers, if you press for the test to be done, ultimately learn information about your child that you later regret knowing. There is an argument, however, that early testing may help a child, and his or her parents, to adapt to the information through a formative period, which ultimately confers the benefits of adjustment and acceptance of the future.

There are conditions, for example, some of the inherited cancer syndromes, where serious problems are rather unlikely to occur in childhood, although on rare occasions have been reported to do so. The benefit of genetic testing in childhood for such conditions lies in knowing whether surveillance/screening in childhood, or in some situations preventive treatment, is indicated. For those who test negative, screening and/or intervention will not be necessary and all parties involved can be relieved about the future with respect to the condition in question. For those who test positive, however, the necessary evidence-based screening or intervention can avert a serious complication in later life.

For late-onset medical genetic conditions for which no surveillance or treatment has been shown to be helpful, it is considered bad practice to carry out *predictive* genetic tests in childhood. The classical paradigm here is Huntington's disease (HD) (a hereditary disorder of the central nervous system that can cause a range of physical, cognitive and psychiatric problems). It follows autosomal dominant inheritance and the offspring of an affected individual are conceived at 50 per cent risk. The condition may declare itself sometime between 30 and 50 years, although for a significant minority the onset is either earlier or later than this. The mutation in the DNA that causes HD is always of the same kind, which makes the test simple and informative in every case. However, the *decision* to be tested is often a complex one. Experience indicates that the majority of those at risk choose not to be tested, or if they do, it is often at a critical juncture in life when the information is crucial to looking ahead – perhaps in relation to employment, retirement, financial planning, relationships or having a child. Not unusually, it is for the sake of the next generation who are contemplating starting their own families. When so much hesitancy about predictive genetic testing for HD is expressed by adults directly at risk, it is clearly inappropriate to remove that decision from children. But in the future, if one can imagine that a new drug becomes available for preventing HD, and it is most efficacious if started early in life, there would be a compelling reason to contemplate predictive genetic testing. There are, of course, other late-onset and devastating neurodegenerative conditions where predictive genetic testing follows exactly the same principles, for example, early-onset familial Alzheimer disease and familial motor neurone disease.

Apart from these examples, the issue of testing children for their "carrier status" of a particular condition also arises. Examples include cystic fibrosis, reciprocal balanced chromosome translocations (balanced *rearrangements* of the chromosomes), and recessively inherited metabolic conditions (e.g. Tay-Sachs disease). In clinical practice, or at least in clinical genetics, the same principles tend to be applied, i.e. testing the child is an abrogation of the child's right to autonomy in later life. It should be noted, however, that there is no real evidence that testing young people for gene carrier status actually causes psychosocial harm, which highlights the fact that existing guidelines are sometimes based on assumptions rather than empirical evidence. It must also be appreciated that parents usually, and naturally, take the view that they have the right to make decisions on behalf of their offspring because they have primary responsibility for their child and they know their child best.

In 1994 the Clinical Genetics Society, the professional group of clinical geneticists in the UK, convened a working party that reported on genetic testing in children. It focused almost exclusively on *predictive* genetic testing (that is, for future health conditions), stating that *diagnostic* genetic testing for conditions presenting in childhood did not present an ethical dilemma. The main recommendations came down against testing a child for an adult-onset inherited condition, and also for resolving carrier status, as outlined above. The recommendations suggested that if carrier testing is deferred until a later time, the health care system and family together have a responsibility to ensure that testing is offered when the child is older.

A fresh exploration of the whole issue of genetic testing in childhood was undertaken by a working party convened by the British Society for Human Genetics (BSHG), which reported in 2010 (the Clinical Genetics Society became a core constituent group of the BSHG in 1994; in 2013, the BSHG became the British Society for Genetic Medicine).

Testing: special issues in adoption?

The 1994 report of the Clinical Genetics Society on the genetic testing of children made the following summary comment on adoption:

> *There are additional factors to be considered with a healthy but "at risk" child referred for adoption, insofar as the results of the testing might influence decisions made on behalf of the child. However, it should not be assumed that genetic (predictive or carrier) testing will be required before a suitable placement can be achieved.*

In the full body of the document, under the heading, 'Issues relating to adoption', the report stated:

We raise the question as to whether there are particular considerations that might justify the genetic testing of a child being considered for adoption, restricting our attention (as elsewhere in this report) to tests of (unaffected) carrier status, and to predictive tests for adult-onset disorders. Prospective adoptive parents may have a keen interest in the genetic status of a child that they are considering for adoption. Like most people (if given the choice), adopters will usually want healthy children, and the adoption agency is under an obligation to gather information about the child's circumstances, including the health of the child and of members of the family. All relevant available information is then given to prospective adopters so that they can make as informed a decision as possible when deciding whether to accept a child. Good practice indicates that all available information should be passed on. Adoptive parents are mostly from the 10 per cent of involuntarily infertile couples, but some will have made a conscious decision to limit their family because of a heritable disorder. Their personal experiences are likely to affect their views on genetic conditions in a prospective adoptive child.

The basic position of the working party, therefore, was very much one of caution, i.e. that adoption should not be assumed to present a particularly special scenario because the best interests of the child are essentially the same as in any stable family situation. However, it definitely left open the possibility that there could be 'particular considerations that might justify the genetic testing of a child being considered for adoption'. Such considerations would include determining whether the child was a carrier of a condition in the birth family, for example, cystic fibrosis or a chromosome translocation, but each situation would have to be looked at on its merits with a full discussion taking place.

The report also paid attention to the very important issue of adoption, and whether it presented special considerations. It comes to a very similar conclusion, leaving the issue open. After all, prospective adoptive parents 'face multiple uncertainties about any child they adopt, and the desire to reduce uncertainty, when this is possible, is understandable'.

As this is the most recent authoritative statement on these issues, the summary recommendations of the report have been provided in full in Appendix 1 of this book. See also Appendix 2 for further comments on adoption made by the working party.

The Practice Note *Genetic Testing and Adoption* (BAAF, 2006) also gives information and advice on these issues.

A high proportion of children being placed for adoption have health issues but successful placements are usually made, as the adoption stories in this volume testify. However, there may be circumstances where a genetic test will clarify some of those health questions and uncertainties prior to a permanent placement, or even early on in the placement, and each case should be taken on its merits.

Most of the issues can be resolved with a full discussion that includes all relevant parties and professionals, and at all times the best interests of the child must of course be paramount.

PARENTING CHILDREN AFFECTED BY A GENETIC DISORDER

DOROTHY MARSH

SARAH LUCAS

Growth Hormone Deficiency – or how a tiny girl helped a family to grow

Dorothy Marsh

In 2008, towards the end of our preparation to become adoptive parents, we were given a tick list, a list of very simple but searching questions about what we, as prospective adopters, would be able to manage in our child-to-be. It was a long list and the choices were: 'No', 'Could not consider', 'Would discuss', and 'Yes, we would consider'.

We were already parents; my husband had three sons who, for many reasons, all lived with us either permanently or for long periods of time. We were open-minded, well-read and self-aware; under no false delusion about what we could cope with – especially after step-parenting three growing boys! We knew that a girl would fit better with our family and wouldn't take "dad time" away from the boys. We knew that it wouldn't be fair to our youngest, aged ten, to bring a child into the house who had a life-limiting condition or who would need lots of medical appointments. So we ticked 'Yes' to most things, 'Would discuss' to the rest and, with a heavy heart, 'No' to anything medical.

And here we are, almost five years later, very proud parents of our amazing daughter, whom I'll call Taylor. She has long blond hair that falls naturally into beautiful ringlets, intense blue eyes, a smile and a giggle that would make the sun shine, an obsession with Barbies and an inability to pay attention to anything in the world when a TV is within sight! She is also generous, kind, empathetic, funny and has Multiple Pituitary Hormone Disorder. She does not grow, feel hunger, cannot heal herself or maintain her own blood sugar. She takes medication three times a day and injects growth hormone every night, and will do so for the rest of her life.

The story of how we went from a "no" on a tick-list to becoming mini-experts on hormone function is the one that I wanted to tell. It's one that prospective adopters, or indeed any parents-to-be, need to hear. It's a story of ordinary people living ordinary lives and doing the best we can to cope with whatever is around the corner.

The adoption process

Having to be approved by the adoption panel was a difficult time for me – I'm sure it is for most of us. My husband, George, is a lovely man of few words, and not one for sharing emotions, especially in public. Approval by the panel was always just a formality for him. For me, it was more than that, more nervewracking for a start, but as a woman without a birth child it was just one more hurdle to leap; yet again, other people would be making decisions that would affect my future. It was just too much. Not known for my ability to stop talking, our social worker asked me if I was OK because I was a little pale. 'You will give George a chance to speak, won't you?' She smiled at me. At this point my lips had stuck to my teeth and I could not swallow. I also smiled but said nothing. The panel members were lovely, very positive about our previous experiences with children, and all in all the meeting was a blur. After waiting around 15 minutes in a side room with our social worker, the Chair of the panel came and told us that they were recommending unanimously that we be approved for adoption. I felt as if my heart had been shocked into life. I cried, of course. Tears of surprise, joy, and of relief. I was going to be a mum.

The exchange day

Three months later we were still waiting for our child. Our social worker kept in touch, popping round on the odd occasion just to check we were OK and to update us and tell us that she was still actively looking for a match. After such an intense time getting all the paperwork together for the home study and for panel, it all felt a little empty now – as if we'd been forgotten. In September, Terry, our social worker, rang to say that the local consortium of authorities had an exchange day planned for 15 October and asked if we would be prepared to attend. These are days when local authorities work together to match children on their books with prospective adopters. They cut out some of the paperwork by gathering together approved adopters with social workers of children with placement orders. However productive, it all felt a tiny bit brutal – held in a church hall with pinboards full of photos and flyers of approved adopters and waiting children. Each authority had a table with leaflets, children's photos and brief details of their history. Our flyer made us laugh out loud because of its estate agent-type language and posed photos – we looked like quite the perfect family! The whole idea of the day made us excited and uneasy in equal measure.

It was about a two-hour drive to the venue and we had been given a time slot to attend. Terry met us in the foyer as we arrived. She was all "suited and booted" and had pink cheeks – 'I've been working for you already, I think I've found her', she said. 'I've been talking to a social worker of a three-year-old girl and she'd like to meet you; do you want to have a look around at the tables first or have a read of the info I've got?'

I remember the earth standing still. I remember breathing very slowly and saying 'No, we'll look at the details you have and meet the social worker now.' Terry passed us an A4 sheet with the photo of a three-year-old girl on top and a few paragraphs about why she needed new parents. We slid into chairs and put the sheet on the table in front of us, frantically reading while Terry went to find the child's social worker.

'You can't have the first one you see', said George. I could hear the worry in his voice. 'It doesn't work like that!'

The paper listed basic information about the child and her birth family. It stated she was a small child with developmental delay, although there were no medical factors to account for this delay. There had been longstanding concerns about the neglect of her health and developmental needs while she lived at home.

It stated that she had made a positive attachment to her foster carer, that she had speech and language delay but that she was receiving help and support. It ended by stating that, 'She requires carers who are able to offer a loving, caring safe environment and are able to put in place firm and consistent boundaries'.

'That's her, that's our daughter, don't you recognise her?' I whispered. George smiled and repeated, 'It's not how things work'.

We had 15 minutes' chat with the child's social worker – my mouth working overtime again, selling us as her parents! The social worker said she would be in touch – all in all it felt a little like a job interview!

We spent another 40 minutes talking to other authorities, collecting flyers about other children, half-heartedly trying to convince ourselves that maybe our child would be here…We ended up with two or three possible contacts in authorities close by but our hearts were already taken. We decided on that day that there was no point holding back, no point trying to protect ourselves from the heartbreak if we weren't chosen. We would deal with whatever fate dealt us – it's a principle we still follow today.

Terry met us to say goodbye. As we left, she handed us the A4 sheet with the little girl's photo. 'No thanks, you keep it on our file', I said. 'If she's the one, she's the one; if she's not, she's not. I'll just obsess if I have a photo to look at!'

Meeting Taylor's social worker

By early November we'd heard nothing more. I decided

to call Terry at the office only to be told that she'd been off work ill since the week after the exchange day! I was heartbroken – if the little girl's social worker had been trying to contact her when she hadn't been there...The next day, a Thursday, I has a phone call at work from Sue, one of Terry's colleagues, telling me that she had taken over Terry's caseload while she was ill. She said she was just checking that we were OK and letting us know that she would be working with us until Terry was better.

Then came the bombshell: 'Taylor's social worker would like to come and talk to you.'

'Is she meeting with any other families?' I asked nervously, fully aware that this does happen.

'No, just you', laughed Sue. 'Oddly enough, they have told us that they want you, and are only seeing you; it's very unusual'.

Sue arranged to bring us Taylor's details that evening and said that she would arrange a meeting after we had read through the paperwork. 'It's rather a large file', she said, her voice trailing off at the end. 'There have been a lot of medical examinations...'

She wasn't joking! She brought a red A4 binder, bulging with medical reports, hospital records, the Child's Permanence Report (CPR), psychological reports and assessments on the birth family and more besides. She went through the basics with us and left it for us to read in detail overnight, saying we should ring her the next day to say yes or no and to give her the reasons why.

It was a long night.

Taylor's history

The reports told a tale of severe neglect, of a tiny child who never smiled and who hadn't grown normally...pages and pages of detailed chronology, tiny snippets with facts that made it heartbreakingly clear that this child needed us. From that point on we were in it to the end – come hell or high water, we would jump over every hurdle and move mountains to bring her home where she belonged.

The medical facts and the family history were very detailed, and so confusing – social worker involvement from ten weeks of age; many hospital admissions for failure to thrive; no weight gain at home but plenty in hospital; a refusal by the birth family to admit that they were at fault; a refusal to engage with social workers, but always willing to attend medical appointments as instructed. Lots of unnecessary medical appointments – the birth mother saying that Taylor could not hear, could not see, could not walk – yet no problems were ever detected except no weight gain, no growth and always doctors commented that they had never seen Taylor smile.

Every time she was admitted to hospital she put on weight and started to interact with nurses. Every time she went home she lost weight and regressed. Then, one January day, her birth mother found two-year-old Taylor unconscious in her bed with vomit on her pillow. An ambulance was called. The true facts are known only to the birth mother, but reports of events differ widely: Taylor had been well the day before but was up late; she'd been off colour but eating; she'd been refusing food but had drunk tea; she'd been sick at 3am and then was left until 2pm when she was found unconscious. After admission to hospital the details become clearer: her blood sugar levels were undetectable, she was unconscious and needed oxygen. On waking she did not interact with anyone, but lay still and did not cry.

The doctors ran every medical test possible, checked for chromosome disorders, genetic conditions, cystic fibrosis, hormone disorders, and metabolic disorders, and one by one every medical cause for her condition was ruled out. On Taylor's first birthday she weighed 10lb and was the length of a three-month-old baby. By two, she was wearing clothes to fit a six-month-old. Then, when Taylor was two years and two months, the doctors finally stepped in and informed social workers that they could not guarantee her safety if she returned home to her birth family: a birth family who still said she was 'just awkward'.

After her birth mother asked to discharge Taylor against medical advice – and complained that the only reason she put on weight in hospital was because the staff were force-feeding her full-fat yogurt that she said she could not find in supermarkets – a police protection order was granted. The courts decided to place Taylor in the care of an experienced foster carer, Christine, and from that moment on her life began.

The medical reports from that time were very important but they still did not fully account for Taylor's lack of growth. Once in foster care she started to put on weight and her development was astounding, but she did not get much taller. Because of the family history, the specialists decided that she was probably suffering from psychosocial dwarfism, also known as maternal deprivation dwarfism. The court reports surmised that it was not worth investigating causes for lack of growth further until she was placed in her permanent family as doctors believed that she would thrive once settled – or as the social workers were to say later, if you love her she will grow.

Our decision

At nine am the next day I rang Sue. 'Yes', I said, 'Yes, yes, yes'.

'Why?', asked Sue.

That threw me! 'Because there is nothing in those reports that tells me we could not cope, nothing that we cannot deal with. She likes animals, parks and books – she is a three-year-old child who needs a normal family life; she needs parents who can carry on with her speech therapy, who are not fazed by medical jargon and who will fight for her with the last breath in their bodies.'

I could almost hear Sue smiling. 'They can meet you early next week – I'll come too, get the kettle on and you'd better start thinking about bedroom furniture and schools'.

The rollercoaster had left the station!

Looking back, the questions about what we could or could not manage became irrelevant the moment we read about Taylor, as irrelevant as they would become to anyone going through pregnancy and hoping for a healthy child. What we wished for was no longer important – what Taylor needed replaced all that.

That was the beginning, then came the social workers, placement officers, link workers, family support workers, foster carers, paediatricians, the agency medical adviser, and finally the matching panel.

A few days after the phone call, the social workers all met in our living room. The night before, we had bathed the dog, painted the hall and stairs and had a carpet laid. At the end of the meeting they said, 'We aren't looking for anyone else; you need to meet her foster carer and her doctor and make sure you are doing the right thing; we've booked a panel date at the start of December so we'd better get things moving.' A week on and we were handed a massive envelope full of photos and found ourselves being bear-hugged by Christine, the foster carer. We talked about Taylor's favourite things, what she enjoyed doing, and at the end of the meeting Christine asked us what we'd like her to have for Christmas, since she would be bringing it along when she moved in with us. She also asked us if she could cut her hair and what style we would like – Taylor's birth mother hadn't allowed her hair to be cut but it hadn't grown properly because of the lack of nutrition so was like fluffy candy floss. All this we found overwhelming, as we wondered what a three-year-old might like and studied photos and thought about hairstyles. I am so grateful to Christine for the year she cared for our daughter. We'll never be able to explain our special relationship fully: she was the first person to love our daughter unconditionally – she taught her how to smile, taught her that adults could be trusted.

We were then bundled round to the hospital to meet the man who had fought for years to protect our daughter-to-be – the doctor who rang social workers, family support workers and health visitors tirelessly to voice his concerns and point out discrepancies. He was a softly spoken man with such kind eyes; he painted a

SECTION II

very detailed picture about Taylor's visits to the hospital with her birth mother. He showed us medical photos; it was very hard; it was a strange meeting. We went over more paperwork and began to realise the enormity of the task ahead. Parenting a child who had not been nurtured was going to be a challenge. Parenting a child who did not know how to be a child was going to test us beyond belief.

The doctor admitted that although they had ruled out most medical reasons for Taylor's failure to thrive, and although the severity of the neglect went a long way to explaining some of the issues, there was still a question mark hanging over her future. No one could say if she would catch up emotionally, physically or developmentally. It was his belief that she would thrive with parents who could help her to be a child, respond to her needs appropriately and could make her smile.

Matching panel was surreal; a few weeks before Christmas, driving through a busy city, sitting in a tinsel-decorated room in a family centre, being asked, 'Why this child, given all her complicated medical history?'

My wonderful, private, strong husband looked at me with glistening eyes and spoke for both of us. 'Because we see her as more than the paperwork and medical reports; she's not complicated at all. She's a little girl, our little girl.'

I guess that today we see that maybe the experts had a greater understanding of the impact an unknown medical future could hold...

We handed over our family book to her social worker

that day – our book included photos of us all and a photo of our sofa, with all of us sitting on it but with enough space for a little addition.

On 5 January, after a hectic Christmas arranging delivery of a princess toddler bed, bedroom furniture, car seat and a pushchair, we finally set off in the icy winds on our two-hour drive to meet our daughter. The windscreen wash had frozen in the pipes and it was so icy that we worried that we'd never get there alive! But get there we did, and with our hearts pushing their way out of our chests we knocked on the door. Christine opened it. 'Hellooooo! Look who's come to see you today', she said, turning her head toward the living room door. There stood the smallest child I have ever seen walking – a tiny blonde doll with her hair in a bob. She turned and ran into the room and George and I looked at each other, our hearts sinking. Seconds later she returned... with two photos in her miniature hands.

'Mummy…Daddy', she shyly whispered, pointing each photo at us.

And the world began to turn on its correct axis.

Life as a new family

Speeding forward through the following year sees us struggling to help Taylor understand that Mummy and Daddy are the bosses – two years without clear parenting have left her distrustful of adults, watchful of strangers and confused about how she is supposed to feel when Mummy leaves the room! Mealtimes are long and drawn out – she was not weaned so cannot chew with any strength. Because she has not been exposed to many foods, she cannot accept strange tastes easily, but she quickly understands that the doctors' instructions that she cannot go without food for more than six hours without the need for medical attention, due to her low blood sugar readings, have left Mummy and Daddy with no choice but to give in when she refuses to eat. None of the normal toddler feeding routines allowed here – she feels no hunger but needs to eat. What a merry dance she can lead us...added to the fact that her weight is being monitored to check that she is thriving with her new mummy and daddy – just what do you do when your child is too emotionally scared to eat but needs to eat for her health?

Social workers were sure that her lack of growth was down to her lack of nutrition; doctors weren't as certain; but no one knew for sure. And I suppose that therein lay the problem – if we had been parenting a birth child, no one would have suspected anything other than a medical cause for her lack of growth and ill health.

With no medical diagnosis and our increasing concern about her height, we decided to press for answers. Taylor started nursery wearing age 12-month clothes. She would cry most of the way there, not because she didn't want to go, but because she wanted to be carried – her muscles were very weak and she had no strength in her legs. Every day people would point at us and comment, 'Ah, bless her, she's too young to be going to school'. Strangers would ask how old she was, what was wrong with her, even going as far as refusing to believe that she was three or four years old. Our good nature began to wear a little thin!

We returned to her birth town to see her specialist and asked for a referral to another hospital – travelling all that way, to a hospital full of painful memories was just too difficult for Taylor. We were referred to a hospital equally far away, but the consultant there had been involved during the care proceedings so was eager to help us. However, it really was just too far to travel. Eventually we found a consultant 40 minutes away from our home and began the long and frustrating process of trying to understand what was wrong with our beautiful daughter.

The new paediatric endocrinologist read through Taylor's medical history, took yet more height and weight measurements – sitting, standing, lying down – and pronounced that he thought she was growth hormone deficient. She had been with us for a year at this point – her nutrition had been maximised as recommended in her court medical reports and still she had not grown. I felt like such a failure as a parent; there had been meeting after meeting when social workers checked up on her eating, her growth, her weight, her development, and questioned every decision we made. Now here was one consultant who believed that we had done everything we could but that it was time for medicine to take over. To hear that there just might be an answer to our prayers, that maybe she could grow, was such relief. Such guilty relief. How could I be happy that Taylor might have a medical condition, that she might need treatment for the rest of her life?

The consultant booked her in for a growth hormone stimulation test the following month and pointed us in the direction of the Child Growth Foundation – an organisation with a website that was to bring such support and change my views of online groups forever!

Growth Hormone Deficiency

The Child Growth Foundation (CGF) website explains Growth Hormone Deficiency (GHD) as: 'Generally occurring when the pituitary gland cannot produce enough growth hormone for the patient to grow normally'.[1] The website also helped me to confirm that Taylor's medical problems run alongside the neglect and abuse she had suffered, further complicating the diagnosis. She had not grown as a baby because of the starvation, and she had intra-uterine growth retardation from before birth, so it became easier to understand why doctors had difficulty making a diagnosis. The CGF explains:

GHD does not affect intra-uterine growth, but from the age of two, or occasionally from birth, growth is slower than normal. In some cases GHD may be hereditary. About three per cent of children with GHD have siblings with the disorder...or one of the parents is affected. Children with GHD are small with normal skeletal proportions, facial appearance and intelligence. They tend to be overweight (although this reduces with growth hormone treatment).

Taylor was very thin because of the neglect, but probably had GHD so did not grow after the age of two – before this age children do not use growth hormone to grow, they use calories.

The National Institute of Clinical Excellence (NICE) will only approve treatment with growth hormones in

[1] www.childgrowthfoundation.org/Default.aspx?page=ConditionsGHD

children after two rounds of testing and a myriad of back-up data – growth charts, MRI scans, etc. So the stimulation tests are necessary before treatment can be started. The growth hormone stimulation tests are also explained on the website: 'The diagnosis is confirmed by measuring the level of growth hormone production in response to a stimulation test which generally requires a morning in hospital'. As it happens, it turned out to be one of the most difficult times in all of our lives.

For Taylor, this meant a day in hospital where blood was taken every hour. Except her veins were too small for the needle; three doctors tried for over an hour, eventually using a dark room and a torch under her hand to insert the needle. Blood was drawn and the samples were labelled with the time and sent off. An hour later the veins had collapsed again and it became even harder to take blood. By the third time, the nurses were having to milk the blood from her arm by squeezing the vein and encouraging the blood out. Taylor sat on my lap, her big blue eyes staring into mine and begged me to stop them hurting her. There are no words to describe her feelings or mine.

Towards the end of the tests the nurses injected her with insulin to artificially lower her blood sugar and test her responses. Even with all the pain, she fell asleep and they had to inject her again to bring her round. On the way home Taylor told us about her first time waking up in hospital with lots of wires attached to her and asked us if we could remember...

Four weeks later the results showed that she produced almost zero growth hormone. They also showed that she did not produce prolactin or sufficient cortisol –

indicating that her pituitary gland was not functioning
correctly. The Society for Endocrinology website
explains:

*The pituitary gland is called the "master gland" as
the hormones it produces control so many different
processes in the body. It senses the body's needs
and sends signals to different organs and glands
throughout the body to regulate their function and
maintain an appropriate environment. It secretes
a variety of hormones into the bloodstream which
act as messengers to transmit information from
the pituitary gland to distant cells, regulating
their activity. For example, the pituitary gland
produces prolactin which acts on the breasts to
induce milk production. The pituitary gland also
secretes hormones that act on the adrenal glands,
thyroid gland, ovaries and testes, which in turn
produce other hormones. Through production of its
hormones, the pituitary gland controls metabolism,
growth, sexual maturation, reproduction, blood
pressure and many other vital physical functions
and processes.* [2]

The endocrine nurse rang us to arrange to come and
see us within days. Cortisol is our bodies' natural steroid
and is necessary to support all internal cell regeneration
and healing – without cortisol Taylor would struggle to
heal from illnesses, and even mild vomiting could prove

---

[2] www.yourhormones.info/glands/pituitary_gland.aspx

fatal as her body would not spring into action to protect itself. We were taught how to inject intra-muscularly, taught how serious this was and shocked into the realisation that our daughter was now dependant on steroids to survive.

We have since learnt that this condition could be genetic (further sleuth work on my part has shown that Taylor's birth father is only 5ft tall), idiopathic (a condition the cause of which is not known or that arises spontaneously) or acquired. MRI tests later that year showed an area of brain damage around the pituitary gland, damage that meant an area of brain did not grow as it should. Further reading of the medical reports revealed a concern about a head injury during initial hospital investigations.

Two months later the tests had to be repeated and our brave girl weathered yet another storm with grace, and in August that year we were taught how to replace her growth hormone by daily injection.

Where are we now?

Taylor is eight years old now, she injects herself every evening and is just about the same height as her friends. She takes two hydrocortisone tablets in the morning and one with lunch and dinner. She is now healthy; bugs and such linger slightly longer than you would expect, but we have a regime to double or triple dose her at these times. Ordinary childhood illnesses are met with slight trepidation because of her compromised immune system, but generally we have learnt not to panic – it's been a hard road getting to this point.

The judge who granted the police protection order was

the same one we stood before two-and-a-half years later as he signed our adoption order.

Taylor's birth mother had another child who, after a shaky start, has now been adopted. We meet with him and his parents a few times a year. He is not growing as he should; whether this is because of his poor early nutrition or because he is growth hormone deficient too is yet to be decided.

Taylor has also been diagnosed as having hearing loss and is the proud owner of two sparkly pink hearing aids – again, it was my sleuth work that discovered that her birth father's family have hearing problems and wear aids too.

Within the past month we have inadvertently discovered that Taylor's birth mother is now registered blind and we are scrabbling to try to find out the genetic implications. Yet again, we are the ones having to ask the questions of people who do not seem keen to answer...Why is there not a legal requirement to provide adopters with a full *ongoing* family medical record for their children? Taylor's birth mother appears to have lost her sight over the past few years; there were notes on file that she had a poorly positioned eye – a squint – but that is a long way from being registered blind. She casually dropped hints about her condition in Taylor's latest letterbox letter – no definite diagnosis, just a veiled discussion about her white stick! It took phone calls and investigations to have her tell the letterbox co-ordinator that maybe we 'ought to be told as it runs in the family'. So we only have her word on the subject – further investigations are clearly going to be needed. It would be nice to think that one day we could just get on with trying to be a family, without the shadow of more revelations hanging over us – or maybe that is the problem? Our efforts to live as a family are perhaps naive given our beginnings – yet many families today are made not by conventional methods but by circumstance. (Note from BAAF: Best practice requires more detailed comprehensive medical information about the birth family than was made available in this case.)

Having thought about adoption as a process, I can see that with the Government agenda to push for earlier intervention and removal of children, there will be more cases like ours – adoptive families who, like birth families, are parenting children who develop medical problems. Birth families almost always have full family histories – they know that Great Aunty Greta was very small and did not grow; they know that as children they had hearing problems; they are more prepared than we are. As much as forewarned may be forearmed, we are forewarned of uncertainties and seem therefore more prepared for things to go wrong. It can take some of the joy away. But things also go right. Taylor's birth family has learning difficulties and we were told from the start that the levels of developmental delay found in Taylor meant an uncertain future. But Taylor is as bright as a button; her area of brain damage means that her working memory is poor and she needs reminding to do everyday things like changing her reading book and brushing her hair and teeth, but don't all eight-year-olds? She is in the highest groups at school for literacy and numeracy, swims, sings, is a Brownie and shows no signs of any learning difficulties. If full genetic testing were available for all adopted children, would we want to be given the results? Would we want to know? Adoption already means living without absolute knowledge of the things that happened to your child before they found their way home to you. For us the answer is no – Taylor is more than just the sum of her genes, she is already living proof that nature and nurture cannot be separated or defined. She is what she is and what she is, is ours.

And the future? Since the pituitary gland produces sex hormones, we do not know if Taylor will reach puberty without more hormone replacement. We do not know if she will be able to have children without assistance, but then again that's hardly the end of the world, just the beginning of a new road.

As parents, we are wiser now. Our relationship with our other children has suffered, not only because of the demands made by the medical issues, but also because it's hard trying to make up for lost time with a child who has been neglected. But if Taylor had been our birth child the medical outcome could still have been similar.

At this point I feel the need to point out that the medical information, whilst daunting, was not the most difficult thing to come to terms with. Now we have lived with our daughter for five years we can read between the lines of the reports, can guess some of the things that cannot be recorded on paper: when a report says 'Has not received enough calories whilst in the birth family', it does not just mean did not have enough food, it means 'was starved'. When a report casually mentions that there is a history of sexual abuse in the family but that a child protection medical proved nothing, it leaves a massive gap in our understanding of what happened to our beautiful child. As Taylor's behaviours begin to point to some form of sexual abuse, our minds have no place to wander other than to those reports...but who, what, why and when have no meaning now because they are questions with no answers. Answers will not make things feel better for her or for us.

We were not foolish – we thought we understood that things would be different, but no one can sufficiently foresee the implications those differences can have for families. Maybe our family would be in the same position today if Taylor had not joined us – who can say? But I know one thing for certain – whatever is round the next corner, we will face it together. We are a family. We are stronger together.

Further information on Growth Hormone Deficiency (GHD)/ Multi Hormone Pituitary Deficiency (MPHD)

www.childgrowthfoundation.org/CMS/FILES/05_ EmergencyInformationPack.pdf

www.childgrowthfoundation.org/default.aspx?page=grow thdisorderbooklets

www.childgrowthfoundation.org/Default. aspx?page=ConditionsGHD

www.nice.org.uk/nicemedia/pdf/HGHinChild-42-ALS.pdf

Who needs cruises? A tale of three daughters

Sarah Lucas

*Our story begins where a romantic novel would end
– young lovers walking along a beach as the sun goes
down, talking about their hopes and dreams for the
future. If you listened in, one of those dreams might
sound rather strange as not many couples would be
talking about adding a child with disabilities to their
future family.*

Fast-forward two years, and you see us facing the difficult
news that our first-born son is severely disabled with
cerebral palsy. Move on another ten years and you find
us with three sons: one highly intelligent nine-year-old
determined not to let his many physical difficulties get in
his way; one hyperactive, school-hating six-year-old who
has decided that sleep is a waste of time; and a three-
year-old, who also doesn't believe in sleep, about to start

pre-school. Add to the mix two sleep-deprived parents with rather more grey hairs than you would expect.

It was at this point that I began to think about what I would do once all the boys were at school. The idea of a fourth home-grown baby was considered and rejected; the idea of my returning to the workplace was not feasible as there was no possibility of out-of-school care for our eldest. To cut a long story short, we became foster carers, with a particular interest in pre-adoption placements for little ones with a disability.

Jenny joins our family

Following a casual remark at a fostering review ('If you have a Down's baby tucked away anywhere, I'd love that'), a tiny, floppy and very poorly baby came into our lives. Jenny had been rejected within hours of her birth because she had Down syndrome, and many initial problems caused by a serious congenital heart condition, Fallots' tetralogy, which would mean major surgery in early childhood. As we talked with her paediatrician, we realised that this was a very serious condition and that without surgery Jenny would die. The hoped-for plan was that Jenny would grow and have surgery when she was about two. As we knew she was going to be placed for adoption, we thought that her new family would be the one to be faced with that enormous hurdle. In the meantime, she was described by the paediatrician as 'the hardest-to-feed Down's baby he had ever seen', so for several months feeding Jenny became the focus of my waking hours. Bottles were abandoned (the effort of sucking was just too much) and hours were spent giving tiny amounts of milk from a teaspoon, and coaxing this scrap of a baby to take a hold on life. Gradually Jenny began to emerge – her first wide smile of recognition, her giggle at the antics of her foster brothers, her first taste of chocolate pudding (a life-long love affair!) and her oh-so-slow physical progress.

Just as caring for Jenny became a little more straightforward, her heart condition worsened, and "blue do's" became a regular feature of her life. Most mornings would bring a time when she was obviously in pain and distress, when there seemed to be nothing I could do other than hold her and love her, and pray that it would soon pass. Naturally, this affected her well-being, she stopped making even the tiniest of weight gains and it became clear that risky surgery was needed sooner than anticipated.

Despite these problems – and maybe in part because of them – each of the boys began to ask, 'Why can't we keep Jenny?' The idea was beginning to take root and grow in our minds; an idea that gave rise to much discussion and heart-searching as well as some arguments and tears. The more we thought, the more possible the idea became. And eventually we were able to see through the barriers other people were putting in our way and clarify how we truly felt. We were well used to caring for a child with a disability and enjoyed the challenges, and we were realistic about the implications of having a child with special needs for life. But as Jenny approached her first birthday and was admitted to hospital for surgery, adoption seemed unimportant compared to what lay ahead. In the hours of surgery, which proved to be even more complex and risky than had been anticipated, and the difficult days afterward when she clung to life by the most slender of threads, it became clear that Jenny was *our* little girl and whatever her problems, we wanted to share them with her. After a week in intensive care, Jenny was able to come off the ventilator. The joy of the moment when she was placed in my arms for the first time after surgery will stay with me forever: here was Jenny – my daughter.

Many years have passed. Jenny has grown into a feisty, funny, food-loving young woman. She has had many more operations, including a new pulmonary valve and several pacemakers, and has knocked on heaven's door on a number of occasions (but heaven must have decided they weren't quite ready for her yet!). She lives at home with us, but has a comprehensive package of support which allows her to be independent, while still "plugged in" to the security of home. With her supporters, she does several hours a week of voluntary work, dances, swims, cooks, goes out for meals, indulges in retail therapy, and much, much more. Being her parents is a privilege and a pleasure, even though we do not know how many more years of life are ahead. I am so thankful that our social worker did have a Down's baby tucked away!

Nadia joins our family

Fast-forward once more, and our family has changed again. Eldest son, having pioneered his way through mainstream education, gained three A-levels, a driving licence, an adapted car and a powered wheelchair, is in a faraway university studying for a master's degree in physics. We had encouraged independence and a belief that disability should never be a barrier, and it wouldn't be right to complain about the lack of phone calls and visits home! The three children left at home, joined by various foster children along the way, were doing OK, and my other half had the happy opportunity to part company with his long-term employers on favourable terms. The idea of golf and cruises was given brief consideration and rejected, leaving space for the idea of adding another special needs child to our tribe.

After a few false starts we came across a picture in *Children Who Wait* of a seven-year-old who seemed to fit the bill. Despite differences in our religion and ethnicity, we were considered a good enough match (possibly the absence of other "takers" might have been in our favour), and in due time we met our new daughter, Nadia. After the briefest of introductions – a foster carer refusing to co-operate and threatening to disrupt the placement – we brought her home and began to discover the extent of her abilities and disabilities. Nadia had been neglected and ultimately rejected by her birth family because of her condition, then had spent time in a children's home followed by three years in a foster family.

Nadia had profound learning disability, was partially sighted, very withdrawn and unable to stand or walk. Several unusual physical features that were obvious from her earliest days suggested a genetic disorder but despite extensive tests, no conclusive evidence was found, and a catch-all diagnosis of Global Developmental Delay was the best anyone could do. We were not unduly concerned about the lack of an accurate diagnosis; perhaps because we were not her birth parents, we were spared the need to find the reason for our child's disability. Nadia settled quickly, and nosily, into our family unit and we found that she was adept at hiding her skills. She discovered that we were not going to let her get away with that, and within a short time she was wearing glasses full-time (and I was developing a deep and meaningful relationship with our local optician), walking, playing with some toys, responding in a much more

SECTION II

83

positive way and relating well to other people. Over the years she honed the art of laziness to perfection, developed the "I'm as blind as a bat until you hide my favourite toy" skill and used her amazing "won't power" in as many ways as her eldest brother used his willpower.

Nadia lived with us until she was 18, when she moved to a house where she is supported full-time by a caring staff team. She is, and will remain, a precious daughter whom we see regularly and whose corner we fight as often and as fiercely as is necessary. Her disabilities are many, her spoken language is non-existent, but her ability to express herself and to inspire deep affection in those who care for her is a testament to her unique and endearing personality.

Two very different daughters, both rejected because of their genetic inheritance which is an integral part of the remarkable people they are. Although there is no question that their genetic conditions are significant, life-changing and ultimately life-limiting, the day-to-day implications are not great. They are our special girls, Jenny and Nadia.

Our family grows again

While Jenny and Nadia were growing up, other changes were happening in the family. Two more sons left home, an elderly parent who lived with us for a number of years died, and various fosterlings came and went. Three years were spent looking after, and loving, a little girl whose early trauma and neglect had damaged her far more than any genetic inheritance could have done. It was after Skye moved to her permanent family that another bright idea began to form in our minds. We had the time, energy and space to offer a permanent home to a straightforward sibling pair. Again, there were false starts and disappointments, but eventually a social worker we were working with and trusted told us of two sisters who were in need of a permanent family. Jane was eleven and Katie seven and both had experienced many years of chaotic neglect before finally being taken into care. Jane was in a children's home and Katie was in a foster placement that was almost at the point of disruption. While we were drawn to these girls, the huge stumbling block was that Katie had cystic fibrosis (CF), a condition we knew a little about and were reluctant to take on. Again, lots of thoughts, discussions, prayer and what ifs, but the equation of a family needing two girls and two girls needing a family was too strong to resist.

So Jane and Katie joined our family. We were well supported by the medical team, who were responsible for Katie's care, but it was a steep learning curve to take on board the amount of treatment and vigilance needed to keep Katie well. CF is a serious, chronic and life-limiting genetic condition for which there is no cure. Treatments have developed over the years that have increased life expectancy, so physiotherapy at least twice a day, a closely monitored high-calorie diet and many medications, as well as numerous hospital appointments, became part of our new routine. At times it felt as if there was an extra, demanding family member called CF. Some things we had anticipated; others came as a surprise. Katie had spent many months in hospital, with her family in residence, and sometimes hospital visits were alarming as she reverted to the "wild child" the moment she walked through the hospital door. Staff knew her well, but they also found it difficult to adjust to the changes in Katie and in her situation – although they were relieved that she had been removed from the environment that had so severely damaged her health.

Working closely with a multi-disciplinary health team meant that sometimes it felt as if we were parenting Katie in a public arena. Because of our experience with our other children, we were quite comfortable with this, but some parents could find it overwhelming.

Over the first months of Katie living with us, we had to learn about the reality of day-to-day life with CF and the measures required to keep her well – a rigorous and relentless timetable of medication and treatment that never allowed a day off and would only increase with time. Another thing that I hadn't considered was the impact of growing to love a child with an illness that would inevitably bring her much suffering and shorten her life. There were times when the feeling of deep sorrow became so all-consuming that I was in danger of letting CF define Katie, rather than seeing her as a child who happened to have a life-limiting health condition. But in other ways CF liberated us – childhood is precious, but how much more so for a child with an uncertain future? It became our goal for "today to be a good day", and if that meant a bit of spoiling along the way, so be it.

Jane and Katie's needs

Alongside these adjustments, another serious problem needed addressing. Although Jane and Katie had been seen by social workers in contact sessions with their birth mother and younger sibling, they had not lived together in care. What had been observed as "closeness" was, in fact, intense competitiveness, rivalry and manipulation. Affectionate hugs were an opportunity for Jane to hurt Katie. Any sign of Katie making an attachment to us had to be vetoed by Jane, who was unwilling and unable to relinquish her control over her sister, and although both girls seemed to be doing quite well, we knew that progress was superficial. Perhaps this was all that Jane could manage, but we and Katie's therapist felt confident that Katie, despite being a chaotic, volatile and exhausting little girl, was able to make a much more secure attachment to us, which would be vital for her physical and emotional wellbeing. Following a thorough assessment of both girls' needs (during which one therapist described feeling so overwhelmed by their demands and competitiveness that he felt unable to drive after 30 minutes with them), the sad decision was made that the girls had to be separated and Jane moved to a long-term foster placement.

Quite quickly Katie relaxed and blossomed and we were in a better position to step back and assess how best to meet her many needs. First of all, we had to face the fact that what we were told was Katie being "behind" was more than that, and she clearly had a learning disability, which of course would make a huge difference to her being able to take on responsibility for her own medical care. While the learning disability wasn't a big issue, the lifelong implications were. Any remaining plans for golf and cruises disappeared over the horizon! And we increasingly felt that Katie needed the security that only adoption could bring. A therapist who worked closely with Katie at this time described her as 'A vulnerable child with a marked delay in her emotional development…with few strategies for dealing with her feelings' and who was 'fearful and resentful about being parented'. This same therapist was quite explicit: 'Katie's success or failure in future life will depend upon an attribute we know as attachment…which develops in

SECTION II

a child who has experienced a predictable pattern of warmth, sensitivity, responsiveness and dependability from a significant caregiver' – all of which strengthened our conviction that nothing less than adoption would give her the security she so desperately needed.

While Jane was with us the plan was permanency through fostering, but Katie's needs were now quite different. While we wanted to adopt her, we were determined not to do so without a support package that recognised her many and complex needs and would allow us to give her the very best of care for as long as possible. The many professionals in her life could see that this was reasonable and yet it took three long years of battling with the authorities to gain agreement to a suitable package of support. One psychologist who worked with Katie wrote: 'The complex and relentless treatment regime for CF is physically and emotionally demanding to both the young person with CF and the adults caring for them…they cope with the stresses of living with a life-limiting and quality of life-reducing illness. They cope with, and adhere to, a demanding treatment regime, and with the ordinary strains of growing up which are made more difficult and can have more serious consequences for a child with CF.' The case for a support package for Katie was indisputable and eventually the long battle was won. Just before her twelfth birthday, Katie became our legal daughter, and the following week she was christened, which sealed her place in our family and her place in our church family. Her carefully chosen (and wonderful!) godparents and their relatives joined us for a day of celebration – a memorable and moving occasion.

Contact issues

So far I have made no mention of Katie's birth family.
She is part of a large multi-generational "clan", headed
by abusive grandparents and well known to social
services. Her birth mother, who has learning disabilities,
had been repeatedly abused and taken advantage of by
the rest of the clan. Like many women with her level
of need, she had numerous partners who also abused
her, and a series of "best friends" who did likewise. She,
and therefore her children, were regularly subjected to
violence and abuse from various male friends and the
wider family. Although she loved her children, there
was no way that she could care for them adequately or
protect them, and Jane and Katie had taken on a parental
role within the family. Perhaps understanding their
birth mother's past made it easier for us to "forgive"
the permanent damage her neglect had done to Katie's
health. But in addition to our strange mix of emotions
in the relationship with the girls' birth mother is an
irrational anger that she (albeit unknowingly) passed on
this dreadful condition.

Contact has been maintained; it has been inevitably
difficult and strained, but seeing her birth mother does
ease Katie's worries about her. The therapist working
with Katie found the revelations she made about life in
her birth family harrowing and was firmly of the opinion
that contact should be stopped – certainly a tempting
idea! But I was acutely aware that it was likely that Katie
would become increasingly ill, and her birth mother and
I could both face and share the pain of losing a dearly
loved daughter. It can only be right for Katie to have
whatever relationship she needs with her birth mother
as she faces the end of life, without any of the baggage
of an emotional reunion. So contact continues, and

SECTION II

Katie has a realistic understanding of her birth mother's limitations – and now, as a young adult, is choosing to see her less often.

While our battles with social services over an adequate support package were in full swing, Katie's health quite suddenly deteriorated for no apparent reason. Her treatment load increased and intravenous antibiotics became a feature of her life after several years without them. As is common with people with CF, Katie's veins were damaged, making the administration of these drugs difficult, and Katie had to undergo many painful and distressing procedures. Although this was deeply upsetting for us both, Katie's trust and reliance on me increased hugely while in hospital. I look back on this as a time when our relationship was sealed and strengthened in a very special way. Katie began to trust that I would be there alongside her, helping her to find strength to deal with the horrible times she was going through. She wasn't alone, and gradually she became less scared of letting herself become attached and dependent on me. Eventually, a surgical procedure allowed IVs to be delivered relatively painlessly and more easily and, with training, I was able to start giving her IVs at home. While this is better for Katie, and less disruptive and unsettling for the rest of the family, it is a tiring and time-consuming task that has for several years dominated life for two weeks out of every twelve, and as she grows older the gaps between her intravenous treatments become shorter.

Growing up

Adolescence is a difficult time for all children, and for adopted children it can be even more challenging, given their poor start in life and slowness in maturing.

Managing and encouraging a teenager's steps towards independence is an important and often nerve-wracking part of the parental journey. In addition to all the usual teenage "stuff", Katie has had to begin to come to terms with her understanding of CF and its implications for her. She sees, but does not always understand, that she is different from her peers and she has to decide how much information to share about her condition. She has to move towards greater independence in managing her treatments as much as she is able to, given the limitations of her learning disability. As her thoughts turn to future relationships, she knows that a partner will have to support her, and she knows that she will probably never be well enough to consider having a child of her own. Perhaps her learning disability shields her from some hard truths, because she is not aware of the risk of passing on her condition to her children.

As her parents, we have to handle her normal teenage rebelliousness – an important part of growing up – giving her freedom to rebel while making sure that she doesn't compromise her health. We have to support her in understanding the implications of her condition and the consequences of not keeping up with her treatments, diet and medication. For any parent of a child with CF, these are enormous challenges, but adding Katie's difficult start in life and her learning disability to the mix sometimes stretches our resourcefulness to the limit.

Now Katie is a young adult. She is in her last year at the special school that she has attended since she was eleven, and she has made some academic progress. She has been given amazing support in overcoming her emotional and behavioural issues. She is no longer the

"diva", the whirlwind of chaos, she once was. Although
still vulnerable, she is increasingly able to make sound
friendship and relationship choices and always tries her
best to make the most of her limited abilities. She has
amazing courage in facing the huge challenges her health
presents, never shows any self-pity and doesn't use her
poor health as an excuse to avoid anything. School staff
describe her as a leader, setting a good example for
others and inspirational in her determination not to let
illness get in the way of everyday life. She is so different
from the frightened and angry little girl who joined our
family and I feel that we have fulfilled the pledge we
made to ourselves, to ensure that Katie had a secure and
happy childhood.

Living with CF

Before I became Katie's parent, I had assumed that
CF was a condition where there was a steady and
generally predictable decline. Now I would describe it
as a condition where you are walking along a cliff edge,
working very hard to keep on the path, which can seem
to be going well for months and sometimes years. Then
suddenly, often without warning, CF blows you off that
path and life takes a turn for the worse. While you hope
that increased treatment will allow you to regain your
foothold on the original path, more often than not it is
another, lower and more challenging path that you find
yourself on. We have recently taken another "fall" which
has increased Katie's treatment burden (and I use that
word deliberately) and has meant that she has had to
undergo many more tests and procedures. Despite this,
her health has worsened significantly in a short period,
and that troublesome family member called CF is making
its presence felt. At the point where a young person
should be looking to the future and its opening doors

with excitement and optimism, Katie has to find ways
to lead a fulfilling life while taking into account physical
limitations. As her parents, we have to find the right
balance of encouraging independence while maintaining
a far greater level of care than is the norm, even among
her learning disabled peers.

This balancing act is enormously challenging, and
something I often feel unequal to. Supporting Katie
as she takes on the reality of life with CF and all its
limitations is painful at times – what parent would not
want to shield their child from all these challenges?
Because of her emotional dependence on us, we are
not able to distance ourselves from this process and
so are not able to protect ourselves from the resulting
sadness. Because of her learning disability, Katie is not
always able to deal with aspects of her care or to work
out strategies to deal with problems. Her relationship
with the adult team now responsible for her care is not
straightforward: we all grapple with the implications of
the gaps in her understanding, especially as treatments
become more difficult and invasive.

The practical and physical demands of Katie's treatments
have increased. Hospital visits are more frequent, and
the number of medications she takes has increased in
quantity and frequency. Liaison with her specialist team
is ongoing, but more in-depth as her treatments are
juggled to keep her as well as possible. More effort has
to be made to encourage Katie to recognise symptoms
and to report and react to them properly. Katie is having
to recognise that her "pot of energy" doesn't allow her
to do everything she would like to, but alongside this
she has to accept that exercise is essential for her health
and has to be high on her list of priorities. Despite a

decreasing appetite, she needs to be encouraged to keep up a high-calorie diet, to help her fight infection. We have to help Katie to find ways to fulfil her ambitions that are achievable and realistic – not by curbing her enthusiasm, but by trying to ensure her goals are within her grasp.

Katie needs to be supported as she accesses adult services that don't always take into account an invisible learning disability and emotional vulnerability, and the impression of being an over-protective parent has to be challenged. I have to be Katie's ears, always ready to observe when she has not understood and to explain or ask for explanations. I have to be Katie's voice, to speak out when she can't or feels unable to – while all the time encouraging her to do so for herself. I have to know when to hold back and when to step forward. I have to be honest in answering Katie's questions about the future, and supportive in helping her to ask difficult questions of her team, but at the same time to be as upbeat and positive as we can be. Above all, we need to work with Katie to make sure that she is living life to the full, despite CF, and is given every chance to mature and develop into a happy and well-adjusted young woman – and we will do everything in our power to achieve this.

So we have travelled eleven years of Katie's childhood, through dressing up and dolls, to Barbies and boy bands, past all things pink and sparkly to a more balanced colour palette. We stay in the land of music and make-up (lots!) and take detours into the land of friends falling out, breaking boy's hearts and often find ourselves lost and confused in the dark forest of social networking. This journey will be recognised by all parents of girls!

But our path is leading us to a very different place. CF

is a progressive illness that will almost certainly lead to Katie's premature death, and will definitely limit her life more and more as she grows older. She will face more frequent treatments, other complications will occur and potentially difficult decisions will have to be made in managing the later stages of CF. The possibility of transplantation (which does not cure, just alters the nature of the condition and adds its own complications) may have to be considered. Because of her lack of perception and joined-up thinking, Katie is only partly aware of this, but inevitably this awareness is growing. Although people with CF do not mix because of the dangers of cross-infection, modern technology allows them to chat online, so Katie finds out when someone is struggling and hears the sad news of another young person's death, and so do we.

It is often said that no parent should outlive their child – but the possibility of this happening is with us every single day. Because of the daily round of treatments, we cannot have a CF-free day, however special or good the day is; that extra family member is there reminding us of its presence. As dreadful as the thought of losing Katie is, perhaps the thought of her outliving us is harder. How would she be able to keep as healthy as possible without the endless support we give her – and how will we be able to continue to do this as we get older? Would she be able to be strong enough to cope with all the hard times she will face without the emotional strength she draws from us? Although there are people in her life who love her very much, would they be able to give her the support she needs? Of course we do not know the answers to these questions, but we have faith that her life and ours is in the hands of a wise heavenly Father who does know what the future holds.

SECTION II

95

So we prepare ourselves for this next stage of our lives together, which will challenge us in many new ways. Katie is learning to be more independent, but we still have to provide the framework in which she can keep safe and well. Again, there is a battle to find the support that our family needs to continue caring for Katie; and great is the frustration that finding enough support always has to be a battle. Although we are now at the age when our contemporaries are enjoying retirement and a more leisurely lifestyle, we are balancing our own needs alongside Katie's and, to a lesser extent, Jenny's dependence on us.

We have been on a long and adventurous journey since that walk along the beach forty years ago. We have travelled on paths that we could not have imagined, but it has been rewarding and satisfying in so many unexpected ways. It is a journey that we have shared with many people who have supported us and walked alongside us, and a journey that has had times of joy and times of sadness. We consider it an enormous privilege to be the parents of all of our children, but to have Jenny, Nadia and Katie in our lives and to help them to reach their potential while facing difficult times has been an amazing experience that has at times had huge costs but has brought rewards beyond measure.

Our golden rules

1. Whatever genetic condition a child has, they are first and foremost a child. They will not be the same as any other child with the condition and their unique personality will shine through.

2. While you will understandably want to find out more about the genetic condition of a child you are thinking

96

of adopting, and many of the reports you will read are likely to focus on this, understanding the child's history, trauma and emotional needs is just as important.

3. Make sure that you have an appropriate support package in place that recognises the life-long commitment needed to care for a child with a genetic disorder. While you are likely to be entitled to disability benefits, this is unlikely to cover the cost of caring for a child with complex needs.

4. Look after yourself! If you are worn out physically and emotionally, the whole family unit will suffer. Invest time in relationships and don't focus entirely on the needs of the child and her condition.

5. Before considering adopting a child with complex needs, be sure that you will be comfortable working with a number of professionals who will inevitably have considerable involvement with your family.

6. If the child has an ongoing medical need, find out where the nearest specialists are – we were fortunate that there were excellent specialist services for both Jenny and Katie within reasonable travelling distance, and this has made life much more straightforward.

7. Try to make contact with other parents, or organisations for people with the particular condition, to find out more about the daily reality of living with the condition.

8. Value your support network. Allow family and friends to be involved in your life and allow them to see when the going gets tough.

9. Live for today! If your child's future is uncertain, make sure that *today* is a good day. Hard times may be ahead, but the future can only be dealt with when it arrives.

10. Be prepared to let go as your child grows up, while recognising that full independence may not be possible. Leaving the parental home isn't the only route – independence is a frame of mind, not an address!

Above all, remember that no one can tell what the future holds, and anyone can become ill or disabled – life is full of uncertainties. For children who are adopted, there may be more unknowns both in their past and their future. A genetic disorder may seem daunting and frightening, but it is only one aspect of a child's life and doesn't change the child's need for a family to call their own.

SECTION II

References

American Society of Human Genetics Social Issues Committee and the American College of Medical Genetics Social, Ethical and Legal Issues Committee (2000) 'ASHG/ACMG statement: genetic testing in adoption', *American Journal of Human Genetics*, 66, pp. 761–67

BAAF (2006) *Genetic Testing and Adoption*, Practice Note, London: BAAF

British Society for Human Genetics (2010) *Report on the Genetic Testing of Children*, Birmingham: British Society for Human Genetics

Jansen LA and Friedman Ross L (2001) 'The ethics of preadoption genetic testing', *American Journal of Medical Genetics*, 104, pp. 214–20

Nuffield Council of Bioethics (1993) 'Genetic screening: ethical issues', London: Nuffield Council of Bioethics

Turnpenny P (ed) (1995) *Secrets in the Genes: Adoption, inheritance and genetic disease*, London: BAAF

Working Party of the Clinical Genetics Society (1994) 'Report on the genetic testing of children', *Journal of Medical Genetics*, 31, pp. 785–97

Useful organisations

For a comprehensive list of genetic disorders, see GeneReviews: www.ncbi.nlm.nih.gov/books/NBK1116/

British Society for Genetic Medicine
A full list of Regional Genetic Centres in the UK, which provide clinical genetics services and genetic counselling expertise, can be obtained from the British Society for Genetic Medicine.
Clinical Genetics Unit
Birmingham Women's Hospital
Edgbaston
Birmingham
B15 2TG
Tel: 0121 627 2634
www.bsgm.org.uk/

Contact a Family
Provides advice, training and parent support groups for the families of disabled children.

209–211 City Road
London
EC1V 1JN
Advice line: 0808 808 3555
www.cafamily.org.uk/

Child Growth Foundation

Provides advice and information on a number of conditions,
including Growth Hormone Deficiency, for affected people and their
families, and information and training for professionals.
21 Malvern Drive
Sutton Coldfield
B76 1PZ
Tel: 020 8995 0257
www.childgrowthfoundation.org/

Cystic Fibrosis Trust

Provides advice, information and an online community for affected
people and their families.
11 London Road
Bromley
Kent BR1 1BY
Helpline: 0300 373 1000
www.cysticfibrosis.org.uk/

Down Syndrome Association

Provides advice, information and training to people affected by
Down syndrome, their families and professionals.
Langdon Down Centre
2a Langdon Park
Teddington
Middlesex TW11 9PS
Tel: 0333 1212 300
www.downs-syndrome.org.uk/

Appendix I

Recommendations/conclusions of the 2010 British Society for Human Genetics report, *Report on the Genetic Testing of Children*

1. Genetic testing in childhood often leads to better management of a child's condition. Where this is the case, for example, where testing aids immediate medical management such as the initiation or cessation of surveillance or treatment, it is unlikely to be contentious. Nevertheless, the possible longer term consequences for the child and family should, where feasible, be discussed prior to testing.

2. Where genetic testing is primarily predictive of illness or impairment in the future, or is predictive of future reproductive risks, a cautious approach

should be adopted. We recommend that in such circumstances testing should normally be delayed until the young person can decide for himself/herself when, or whether, to be tested. The rationale for this recommendation is that testing in childhood removes the opportunity of the future young person to make their own choices about such decisions, and that opportunity should not be denied to them without good reason.

3. This does not mean that childhood testing for such conditions should never be done. For any particular child and family, the benefits of testing in childhood may outweigh the harms, but we believe that predictive genetic testing for a later onset condition should only happen when there are specific reasons not to wait until a child is older.

4. In each case where parents request genetic testing of a child when this is of no direct or immediate medical benefit, an assessment should be made of the balance of harms and benefits of such testing, taking into account that decisions ought to be made in the child's best interests.

5. Even where a condition is likely to manifest during childhood, the principle of adopting a cautious approach still applies as there may be good reasons to defer testing until the child can participate in discussions. Where there is no realistic possibility of choice being exercised by the future young person before the condition might present clinically, the reasons to defer are weaker.

6. In many situations, therefore, an immediate decision

about testing is unlikely to do justice to the complexity of the issues; ample time for discussion and consideration of the timing of a test with all relevant parties should be allowed. Health care professionals and parents should be enabled to spend time discussing the optimal timing of a predictive genetic test and facilitate, where appropriate, discussions within the family. Encouraging parents to talk to their children about their family history from a young age, so that they grow up knowing about it, will be integral to discussions about genetic testing.

Appendix 2

Comments on adoption from the British Society for Human Genetics report, *Report on the Genetic Testing of Children* (p. 12)

The 1994 guidance recommended that genetic testing should only be carried out on a child being considered for adoption when this would also be done (at that stage) if the child was with his or her birth family. It was suggested, however, that this may not hold for predictive tests if it proves difficult to place a child for adoption because of the uncertainty of her or his genetic status; in this scenario, it was felt that the decision to put the child forward for adoption or to undertake genetic testing would need to be reconsidered. The BMA, GIG (Genetic Interest Group, now known as Genetic Alliance UK) and the American Society for Human Genetics have a somewhat different opinion about this issue, and hold that the same approach should apply as does for children with their birth families.

Applying the same approach for adopted children may not recognise the importance of matching the child and the prospective parents. It is crucial that children should be placed with parents willing and able to care for them in order to minimise the risk of the relationship breaking down. Most parents-to-be would prefer to have a healthy child, and it would seem reasonable to assume this is the case for adoptive parents. However, almost 50 per cent of children needing placement with a family have health problems. These include physical disabilities, developmental delay, learning difficulties, behaviour problems and genetic conditions (including being at risk of an inherited disorder). The evidence suggests that children with these problems can be successfully adopted, particularly when the adopting parents are aware of what they will be facing as a family.

A family willing to adopt a child at risk of an inherited disorder and to find out about their genetic status over time, as in the biological family, appears preferable to a family that sets genetic conditions upon accepting a child. On the other hand, adopting parents face multiple uncertainties about any child they adopt, and the desire to reduce uncertainty, when this is possible, is understandable. We think that there may be special circumstances which mean that genetic tests are undertaken for adoptive children, although they would not be carried out at that stage for children in the care of their birth families. Even so, we recommend caution for carrier testing (of future reproductive significance only) and even more so for predictive testing for later onset conditions (with no useful medical interventions in childhood).

One approach to genetic testing prior to adoption is to recommend that genetics professionals have an open discussion with the prospective parents. Testing then would not occur before prospective parents had met the child or while the child was being "advertised". This would create the opportunity for the specific genetic risks to the child being placed in the context of the background risks faced by any child and parent, and the additional potential risks to the child which may result from genetic testing. Such open discussions often resolve the difficulties without the need for genetic testing of a young child being considered for adoption. In the event of a persisting disagreement between the clinical genetics team and social services, it may be helpful to involve the relevant Trust's legal team. We have heard of cases where courts have ordered the genetic testing of children before it would have been of medical benefit and believe that improved discussions between the different teams involved might avoid such situations. Helpful advice is also available from the British Association of Adoption and Fostering.

[NB. Citations for references have been removed]